All the Words to All the Songs in
The Reader's Digest

CHILDREN'S SONGBOOK

The Reader's Digest Association, Inc.
Pleasantville, New York · Montreal

Copyright © 1985 The Reader's Digest Association, Inc.
Copyright © 1985 The Reader's Digest Association (Canada) Ltd.
Copyright © 1985 Reader's Digest Association Far East Ltd.
Philippine Copyright 1985 Reader's Digest Association Far East Ltd.

Printed in the United States of America
Second Printing, February 1988

GUITAR DIAGRAMS FOR CHORDS USED IN READER'S DIGEST *CHILDREN'S SONGBOOK*

These diagrams include *every basic* chord used in the book. As a general rule, numbers in parentheses, as G(7) or (9), may be omitted if they present difficulties. This would apply also to people who play chord organs and autoharps with a limited selection of chords.

SUBSTITUTE CHORDS: If a chord is not listed here, use the *substitute chord* shown in the book, in parentheses. For example, you may run into Bm7-5 (G7) — you can substitute the G7 for the B minor 7th with a lowered 5th. They have three of the same notes.

BASS NOTES INDICATED IN THE BOOK: For example, D7/G — G is the bass note to be played *on keyboards* or by bass players. However, guitarists may ignore this and play the basic chord as in the diagram — D7 or even simple D.

FOR FURTHER SIMPLIFICATION: Chords that appear by themselves in parentheses may be omitted. For example, one measure $\begin{bmatrix} \text{reads C/E} & / & \text{(D\#dim)} & / \text{ .} \\ \text{(beats 1} & 2 & 3 & 4 \text{).} \end{bmatrix}$ This would call for a C chord with E as the bass note, for two beats; then a D# diminished chord for two beats. But *you* can play a basic C chord for the entire measure.

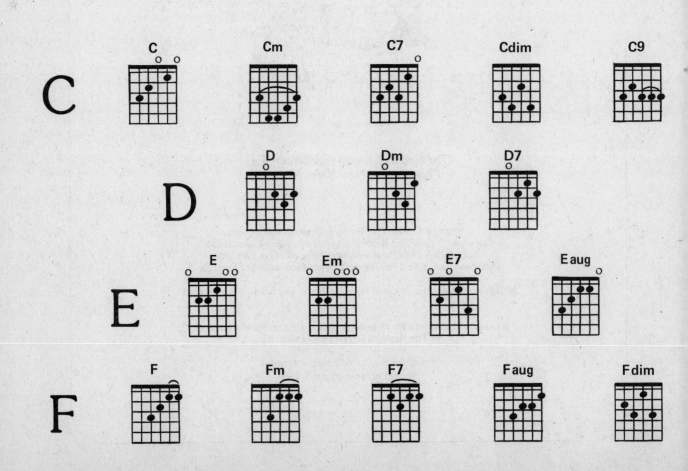

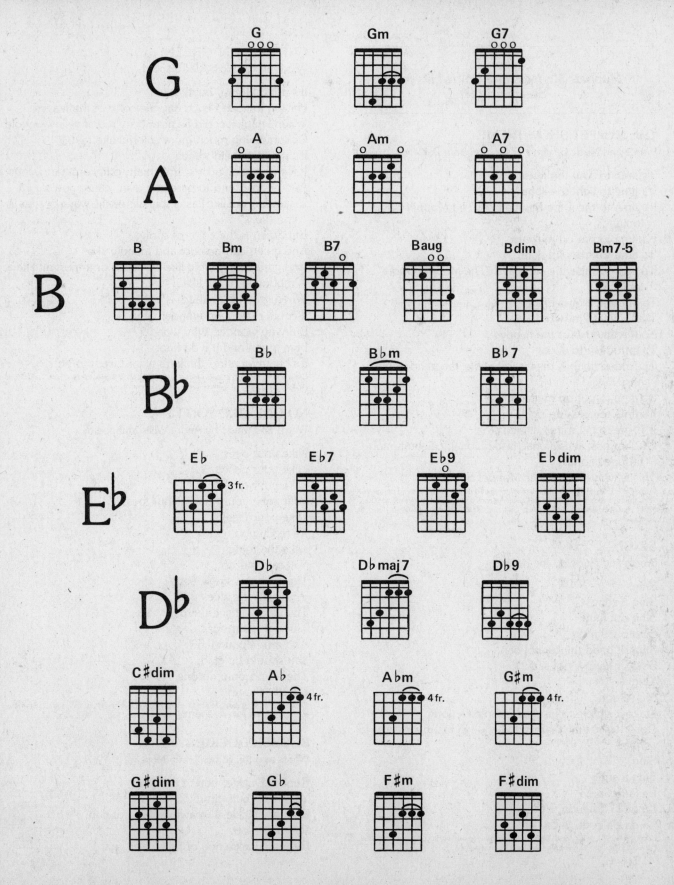

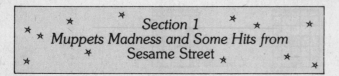

THE MUPPET SHOW THEME
Words and Music by Jim Henson and Sam Pottle

It's time to play the music;
It's time to light the lights;
It's time to meet the Muppets on *The Muppet Show*
   tonight.
It's time to put on makeup;
It's time to dress up right;
It's time to raise the curtain on *The Muppet Show*
   tonight.
To introduce Miss Piggy,
That's what I'm here to do.
So it really makes me happy
To introduce to you
The indescribable, the incompatible, the unadorable . . .
   Miss Piggy!
It's time to put on makeup;
It's time to dress up right;
It's time to get things started
On the most sensational, inspirational, celebrational,
   muppetational . . .
This is what we call *The Muppet Show.*

SING!
Words and Music by Joe Raposo

Sing!
Sing a song,
Sing out loud,
Sing out strong.
Sing of good things, not bad;
Sing of happy, not sad.
Sing!
Sing a song,
Make it simple to last your whole life long.
Don't worry that it's not good enough for anyone else to
   hear.
Sing!
Sing a song.
La la do la da,
La da la do la da,
La da da la do la da.

GREEN (BEIN' GREEN)
Words and Music by Joe Raposo

It's not that easy bein' green,
Having to spend each day the color of the leaves,
When I think it could be nicer bein' red or yellow or gold
Or something much more colorful like that.
It's not easy bein' green;
It seems you blend in with so many other ordinary things,
And people tend to pass you over 'cause you're not
   standing out like flashy sparkles on the water or stars in
   the sky.
But green is the color of spring,
And green can be cool and friendly-like,
And green can be big like an ocean or important like a
   mountain or tall like a tree.
When green is all there is to be,
It could make you wonder why,
But why wonder, why wonder?
I am green and it'll do fine;
It's beautiful and I think it's what I want to be.

NO ONE LIKE YOU
Words and Music by Andra Willis Muhoberac

I like your eyes;
I like your nose;
I like your mouth,
Your ears, your hands, your toes.
I like your face,
It's really you;
I like the things
You say and do.
There's not a single soul
Who sees the skies
The way you see them
Through your eyes.
And aren't you glad?
You should be glad;
There's no one, no one
Exactly like you.

RUBBER DUCKIE
Words and Music by Jeffrey Moss

Rubber Duckie, you're the one;
You make bath time lots of fun.
Rubber Duckie, I'm awfully fond of you,
Vo-vo-dee-oh.
Rubber Duckie, joy of joys,

When I squeeze you, you make noise.
Rubber Duckie, you're my very best friend, it's true.
Oh, ev'ry day when I make my way to the tubby,
I find a little fellow who's cute and yellow and chubby,
Rub-a-dub-dubby.
Rubber Duckie, you're so fine,
And I'm lucky that you're mine.
Rubber Duckie, I'm awfully fond of you.

REPEAT FIRST 13 LINES

Rubber Duckie, I'd like a whole pond of;
Rubber Duckie, I'm awfully fond of you.
Quack!

I LOVE TRASH
Words and Music by Jeffrey Moss

CHORUS
Oh, I love trash,
Anything dirty or dingy or dusty,
Anything ragged or rotten or rusty.
Oh, I love trash.

I have here a sneaker that's tatter'd and worn;
It's all full of holes and the laces are torn,
A gift from my mother the day I was born.
I love it because it's trash.
Yes,
CHORUS

I have here some newspaper thirteen months old.
I wrapped fish inside it; it's smelly and cold.
But I wouldn't trade it for a big pot of gold.
I love it because it's trash.
Yes,
CHORUS

I've a clock that won't work and an old telephone,
A broken umbrella, a rusty trombone,
And I am delighted to call them my own.
I love it because it's trash.
Yes,

I love trash,
Anything dirty or dingy or dusty,
Anything ragged or rotten or rusty.
Oh, I love trash.
Yes, I love,
I love trash.

THE RAINBOW CONNECTION
from *The Muppet Movie*
Words and Music by Paul Williams and Kenny Ascher

Why are there so many songs about rainbows,
And what's on the other side?
Rainbows are visions but only illusions,
And rainbows have nothing to hide.
So we've been told, and some choose to believe it;
I know they're wrong; wait and see.
Someday we'll find it, the rainbow connection,
The lovers, the dreamers and me.
Who said that ev'ry wish would be heard and answered
When wished on the morning star?
Somebody thought of that, and someone believed it;
Look what it's done so far.
What's so amazing that keeps us stargazing,
And what do we think we might see?
Someday we'll find it, the rainbow connection,
The lovers, the dreamers and me.
All of us under its spell;
We know that it's probably magic.
Have you been half asleep and have you heard voices?
I've heard them calling my name.
Is this the sweet sound that calls the young sailors?
The voice might be one and the same.
I've heard it too many times to ignore it;
It's something that I'm s'posed to be.
Someday we'll find it, the rainbow connection,
The lovers, the dreamers and me.
La da da dee
Da da do
La la da da
Da de da do.

Section 2
Songs from Some Favorite Movies and Shows

TOMORROW
from *Annie*
Words by Martin Charnin; Music by Charles Strouse

The sun'll come out tomorrow,
Bet your bottom dollar that tomorrow
There'll be sun.
Jus' thinking about tomorrow
Clears away the cobwebs and the sorrow
Till there's none.

(continued on next page)

When I'm stuck with a day
That's gray and lonely,
I just stick out my chin
And grin and say,
"Oh, the sun'll come out tomorrow,
So you've got to hang on till tomorrow
Come what may.
Tomorrow, tomorrow,
I love ya tomorrow,
You're always a day away."

DING-DONG! THE WITCH IS DEAD

from *The Wizard of Oz*
Words by E. Y. Harburg; Music by Harold Arlen

Ding-dong, the witch is dead!
Which old witch?
The wicked witch.
Ding-dong, the wicked witch is dead.
Wake up, you sleepyhead,
Rub your eyes,
Get out of bed;
Wake up, the wicked witch is dead!
She's gone where the goblins go below,
Below, below, yo-ho,
Let's open up and sing
And ring the bells out.
Ding-dong! the merry-o,
Sing it high,
Sing it low.
Let them know
The wicked witch is dead.

IF I ONLY HAD A BRAIN
(IF I ONLY HAD A HEART)
(IF I ONLY HAD THE NERVE)

from *The Wizard of Oz*
Words by E. Y. Harburg; Music by Harold Arlen

(Scarecrow)
I could while away the hours conferrin' with the flow'rs,
    consultin' with the rain,
And my head I'd be scratchin' while my thoughts were
    busy hatchin'
If I only had a brain.
I'd unravel ev'ry riddle for any individle in trouble or in
    pain.
With the thoughts I'd be thinkin', I could be another
    Lincoln

If I only had a brain.
Oh, I could tell you why the ocean's near the shore;
I could think of things I never thunk before,
And then I'd sit
And think some more.
I would not be just a nuffin', my head all full of stuffin', my
    heart all full of pain.
And perhaps I'd deserve you and be even worthy of you
If I only had a brain.

(Tin Woodman)
When a man's an empty kettle, he should be on his
    mettle and yet I'm torn apart.
Just because I'm presumin' that I could be kinda human
If I only had a heart.
I'd be tender; I'd be gentle and awful sentimental
    regarding love and art.
I'd be friends with the sparrows and the boy that shoots
    the arrows
If I only had a heart.
Picture me, a balcony, above a voice sings low,
"Wherefore art thou, Romeo?"
I hear a beat.
How sweet!
Just to register emotion, jealousy, devotion, and really
    feel the part,
I would stay young and chipper, and I'd lock it with a
    zipper
If I only had a heart.

(Cowardly Lion)
Life is sad, believe me missy, when you're born to be a
    sissy without the vim and verve,
But I could change my habits, nevermore be scared of
    rabbits
If I only had the nerve.
I'm afraid there's no denyin' I'm just a dandylion, a fate I
    don't deserve,
But I could show my prowess, be a lion not a mowess
If I only had the nerve.
Oh, I'd be in my stride, a king down to the core;
Oh, I'd roar the way I never roared before,
And then I'd rrrwoof
And roar some more.
I would show the dinosaurus who's king around the
    fores', a king they'd better serve.
Why with my regal beezer, I could be another Caesar
If I only had the nerve.

OVER THE RAINBOW

from *The Wizard of Oz*
Words by E. Y. Harburg; Music by Harold Arlen

Somewhere over the rainbow way up high,
There's a land that I heard of once in a lullaby.
Somewhere over the rainbow skies are blue,
And the dreams that you dare to dream really do come
    true.
Someday I'll wish upon a star and wake up where the
    clouds are far behind me.
Where troubles melt like lemon drops, away above the
    chimney tops,
That's where you'll find me.
Somewhere over the rainbow bluebirds fly,
Birds fly over the rainbow,
Why then, oh why can't I?
If happy little bluebirds fly beyond the rainbow,
Why, oh why can't I?

WE'RE OFF TO SEE THE WIZARD
(THE WONDERFUL WIZARD OF OZ)

from *The Wizard of Oz*
Words by E. Y. Harburg; Music by Harold Arlen

Follow the yellow brick road;
Follow the yellow brick road;
Follow, follow, follow, follow,
Follow the yellow brick road.
Follow the rainbow over the stream;
Follow the fellow who follows a dream;
Follow, follow, follow, follow,
Follow the yellow brick road.
We're off to see the Wizard,
The wonderful Wizard of Oz.
We hear he is a Whiz of a Wiz,
If ever a Wiz there was.
If ever, oh, ever a Wiz there was,
The Wizard of Oz is one becoz,
Becoz, becoz, becoz, becoz, becoz,
Becoz of the wonderful things he does.
(whistle)
We're off to see the Wizard,
The wonderful Wizard of Oz.

THE INCH WORM

from *Hans Christian Andersen*
Words and Music by Frank Loesser

Two and two are four,
Four and four are eight;
That's all you have on your bus'nesslike mind.
Two and two are four,
Four and four are eight;
How can you be so blind?
Two and two are four,
(Inch worm, inch worm,)
Four and four are eight,
(Measuring the marigolds,)
Eight and eight are sixteen,
(You and your arithmetic,)
Sixteen and sixteen are thirty-two,
(You'll probably go far.)
Two and two are four,
(Inch worm, inch worm,)
Four and four are eight,
(Measuring the marigolds,)
Eight and eight are sixteen,
(Seems to me you'd stop and see)
Sixteen and sixteen are thirty-two.
(How beautiful they are.)

ON THE GOOD SHIP LOLLIPOP

from *Bright Eyes*
Words and Music by Sidney Clare and Richard A. Whiting

On the good ship Lollipop,
It's a sweet trip to a candy shop,
Where bonbons play
On the sunny beach of Peppermint Bay.
Lemonade stands ev'rywhere,
Cracker Jack bands fill the air,
And there you are,
Happy landing on a chocolate bar.
See the sugar bowl do a tootsie roll
With the big bad devil's food cake.
If you eat too much, ooh! ooh!
You'll awake with a tummy ache.
On the good ship Lollipop,
It's a night trip, into bed you hop
With this command:
"All aboard for Candy Land."

DO-RE-MI

from *The Sound of Music*
Words by Oscar Hammerstein II; Music by Richard Rodgers

Doe, a deer, a female deer;
Ray, a drop of golden sun;
Me, a name I call myself;
Far, a long, long way to run;
Sew, a needle pulling thread;
La, a note to follow sew;
Tea, a drink with jam and bread;
That will bring us back to do-oh-oh-oh!
DO, RE, MI, FA, SO, LA, TI, DO!

I WHISTLE A HAPPY TUNE

from *The King and I*
Words by Oscar Hammerstein II; Music by Richard Rodgers

Whenever I feel afraid,
I hold my head erect
And whistle a happy tune,
So no one will suspect I'm afraid.
While shivering in my shoes,
I strike a careless pose
And whistle a happy tune,
And no one ever knows I'm afraid.
The result of this deception is very strange to tell,
For when I fool the people I fear,
I fool myself as well!
I whistle a happy tune
And every single time,
The happiness in the tune
Convinces me that I'm not afraid.
Make believe you're brave,
And the trick will take you far.
You may be as brave
As you make believe you are.
(whistle)
You may be as brave
As you make believe you are.

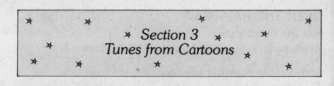

*Section 3
Tunes from Cartoons*

WHO'S AFRAID OF THE BIG BAD WOLF?

from *The Three Little Pigs*
Words and Music by Frank E. Churchill;
Additional words by Ann Ronell

Who's afraid of the big bad wolf, big bad wolf, big bad
  wolf?
Who's afraid of the big bad wolf?
Tra la la la la.
Who's afraid of the big bad wolf, big bad wolf, big bad
  wolf?
Who's afraid of the big bad wolf?
Tra la la la la.
Long ago there were three pigs,
Little handsome piggy-wigs.
For the big bad, very big, very bad wolf,
They didn't give three figs.
Number One was very gay,
And he built his house with hay.
With a hey-hey toot, he blew on his flute,
And he played around all day.
Number Two was fond of jigs,
And so he built his house with twigs.
Heigh-diddle-diddle, he played on his fiddle
And danced with lady pigs.
Number Three said, "Nix on tricks;
I will build my house with bricks."
He had no chance to sing and dance
'Cause work and play don't mix!
Ha-ha ha!
The two little, do little pigs
Just winked and laughed ha-ha!
Came the day when fate did frown,
And the wolf blew into town.
With a gruff "puff-puff," he puffed just enough,
And the hay house fell right down.
One and Two were scared to death
Of the big bad wolfie's breath.
"By the hair of your chinny-chin, I'll blow you in,"
And the twig house answered yes.
No one left but Number Three
To save the piglet family.
When they knocked, he fast unlocked
And said, "Come in with me!"
Now they all were safe inside,
And the bricks hurt wolfie's pride.

So he slid down the chimney and, oh, by jiminy,
In the fire he was fried!
Ha-ha ha!
The three little, free little pigs
Rejoiced and laughed ha-ha!
Who's afraid of the big bad wolf, big bad wolf, big bad
  wolf?
Who's afraid of the big bad wolf?
Tra la la la la.
Who's afraid of the big bad wolf, big bad wolf, big bad
  wolf?
Who's afraid of the big bad wolf?
Tra la la la la.

WHEN I SEE AN ELEPHANT FLY
from *Dumbo*
Words by Ned Washington; Music by Oliver Wallace

I saw a peanut stand, heard a rubber band;
I saw a needle that winked its eye.
But I think I will have seen ev'rything
When I see an elephant fly.
I saw a front porch swing, heard a diamond ring;
I saw a polka-dot railroad tie.
But I think I will have seen ev'rything
When I see an elephant fly.
I saw a clotheshorse rar' up and buck.
They tell me that a man made a veg'table "truck";
I didn't see that, I only heard,
But just to be sociable, I'll take their word.
I saw a lantern slide, saw an old cowhide,
And I just laugh'd till I thought I'd die.
But I think I will have seen ev'rything
When I see an elephant fly.

I saw a garden walk, a banana stalk;
I saw a pig with an awful sty.
But I think I will have seen ev'rything
When I see an elephant fly.
I saw the sugar bowl, saw the jelly roll;
I saw a picket fence, that's no lie.
But I think I will have seen ev'rything
When I see an elephant fly.
I even heard a chocolate drop;
I went into a store, saw a bicycle shop.
You can't deny the things that you see,
But I know there's certain things that just can't be.
The other day by chance saw an old barn dance,
So I'm a gullible sort of guy.
But I think I will have seen ev'rything
When I see an elephant fly.

WITH A SMILE AND A SONG
from *Snow White and the Seven Dwarfs*
Words by Larry Morey; Music by Frank Churchill

With a smile and a song,
Life is just like a bright sunny day.
Your cares fade away,
And your heart is young.
With a smile and a song,
All the world seems to waken anew,
Rejoicing with you
As the song is sung.
There's no use in grumbling
When raindrops come tumbling;
Remember you're the one
Who can fill the world with sunshine.
When you smile and you sing,
Ev'rything is in tune and it's spring,
And life flows along
With a smile and a song.

WHISTLE WHILE YOU WORK
from *Snow White and the Seven Dwarfs*
Words by Larry Morey; Music by Frank Churchill

Just whistle while you work.
(whistle)
Put on that grin and start right in
To whistle loud and long.
Just hum a merry tune.
(hum)
Just do your best, then take a rest
And sing yourself a song.
When there's too much to do,
Don't let it bother you.
Forget your trouble, try to be
Just like the cheerful chickadee.
And whistle while you work.
(whistle)
Come on, get smart, tune up and start
To whistle while you work.
(whistle)

ONE SONG
from *Snow White and the Seven Dwarfs*
Words by Larry Morey; Music by Frank Churchill

One song,
I have but one song,
One song
Only for you.

(continued on next page)

One heart
Tenderly beating,
Ever entreating,
Constantly true.
One love
That has possessed me,
One love
Thrilling me through.
One song,
My heart keeps singing
Of one love
Only for you.

(THE DWARFS' MARCHING SONG) "HEIGH-HO"

from *Snow White and the Seven Dwarfs*
Words by Larry Morey; Music by Frank Churchill

"Heigh-ho," "heigh-ho,"
To make your troubles go,
Just keep on singing all day long
"Heigh-ho," "heigh-ho."
"Heigh-ho," "heigh-ho," "heigh-ho,"
For if you're feeling low,
You positively can't go wrong
With a "heigh," "heigh-ho,"
"Heigh-ho," "heigh-ho," "heigh-ho,"
It's home from work we go,
(whistle)
"Heigh-ho," "heigh-ho,"
"Heigh-ho," "heigh-ho," "heigh-ho,"
All seven in a row,
(whistle)
With a "heigh," "heigh-ho."

THE SILLY SONG (THE DWARFS' YODEL SONG)

from *Snow White and the Seven Dwarfs*
Words by Larry Morey; Music by Frank Churchill

I'd like to dance and tap my feet,
But they won't keep in rhythm.
You see, I washed them both today,
And I can't do nothin' with 'em.

CHORUS
Ho hum, the tune is dumb,
The words don't mean a thing.
Isn't this a silly song
For anyone t' sing?
The minute after I was born,
I didn't have a nightie.
So I tied my whiskers round my legs

And used them for a didie.
CHORUS

I chased a polecat up a tree,
Way out upon a limb,
An' when he got the best o' me,
I got the worst o' him.
CHORUS

We used to have a billy goat;
We had him disinfected.
He could have slept in Grumpy's bed,
But the billy goat objected.
CHORUS

Isn't this a silly song,
Yes, isn't this a silly song,
Yes, isn't this a silly song
For anyone to sing?

HI-DIDDLE-DEE-DEE
(AN ACTOR'S LIFE FOR ME)

from *Pinocchio*
Words by Ned Washington; Music by Leigh Harline

Hi-diddle-dee-dee,
An actor's life for me:
A high silk hat and a silver cane,
A watch of gold with a diamond chain.
Hi-diddle-dee-doo,
You sleep till after two.
You promenade with a big cigar;
You tour the world in a private car;
You dine on chicken and caviar,
An actor's life for me.

GIVE A LITTLE WHISTLE

from *Pinocchio*
Words by Ned Washington; Music by Leigh Harline

When you get in trouble
And you don't know right from wrong,
Give a little whistle *(whistle)*,
Give a little whistle *(whistle)*.
When you meet temptation
And the urge is very strong,
Give a little whistle *(whistle)*,
Give a little whistle *(whistle)*.
Not just a little squeak,
Pucker up and blow.
And if your whistle's weak,
Yell "Jiminy Cricket!"

Take the straight and narrow path
And if you start to slide,
Give a little whistle *(whistle)*,
Give a little whistle *(whistle)*,
And always let your conscience be your guide.

YELLOW SUBMARINE
from *Yellow Submarine*
Word and Music by John Lennon and Paul McCartney

In the town
Where I was born
Lived a man
Who sailed the sea,
And he told
Us of his life
In the land
Of submarines.
So we sailed
Up to the sun
Till we found
The sea of green,
And we lived
Beneath the waves
In our yellow submarine.

CHORUS
We all live in a yellow submarine,
Yellow submarine,
Yellow submarine.
We all live in a yellow submarine,
Yellow submarine,
Yellow submarine.

And our friends
Are all aboard;
Many more of them
Live next door.
And the band begins to play:
CHORUS

As we live
A life of ease,
Ev'ryone of us
Has all we need,
Sky of blue
And sea of green
In our yellow submarine.
CHORUS

I'M POPEYE THE SAILOR MAN
Words and Music by Sammy Lerner

I'm (He's) Popeye the Sailor Man;
I'm (He's) Popeye the Sailor Man.
I'm (He's) strong to the "finich"
'Cause I (he) eats me (his) spinach;
I'm (He's) Popeye the Sailor Man.
I'm (He's) one tough gazookus
Which hates all palookas
Wot ain't on the up and square.
I (He) biffs 'em and buffs 'em
An' always out-roughs 'em,
An' none of 'em gits nowhere.
If anyone dasses to risk my (his) "fisk,"
It's "boff" an' it's "wham," un'erstan'?
So keep good behavior,
That's your one lifesaver
With Popeye the Sailor Man.
I'm (He's) Popeye the Sailor Man;
I'm (He's) Popeye the Sailor Man.
I'm (He's) strong to the "finich"
'Cause I (he) eats me (his) spinach;
I'm (He's) Popeye the Sailor Man.

CASPER THE FRIENDLY GHOST
Words by Mack David; Music by Jerry Livingston

Casper the friendly ghost,
The friendliest ghost you know.
Though grownups might look at him with fright,
The children all love him so.
Casper the friendly ghost,
He couldn't be bad or mean.
He'll romp and play, sing and dance all day,
The friendliest ghost you've seen.
He always says "Hello,"
And he's really glad to meet cha.
Wherever he may go,
He's kind to ev'ry living creature.
Grownups don't understand
Why children love him the most,
But kids all know that he loves them so,
Casper the friendly ghost.

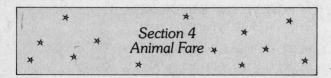

(HOW MUCH IS) THAT DOGGIE IN THE WINDOW
Words and Music by Bob Merrill

CHORUS
How much is that doggie in the window,
The one with the waggly tail?
How much is that doggie in the window?
I do hope that doggie's for sale.

I must take a trip to California
And leave my poor sweetheart alone.
If he has a dog, he won't be lonesome,
And the doggie will have a good home.
CHORUS

I read in the papers there are robbers
With flashlights that shine in the dark.
My love needs a doggie to protect him
And scare them away with one bark.
CHORUS

MY DOG'S BIGGER THAN YOUR DOG
Words and Music by Tom Paxton

My dog's bigger than your dog;
My dog's bigger than yours.
My dog's bigger and he chases mailmen.
My dog's bigger than yours.
My dad's tougher than your dad;
My dad's tougher than yours.
My dad's tougher and he yells louder and
My dad's tougher than yours.

CHORUS
I'm not afraid of the dark anymore;
I can tie my shoes.
I have been to the country,
And I am going to school.

Our car's faster than your car;
Our car's faster than yours.
It has a loud horn; it bumps the other cars.
Our car's faster than yours.
My mom's older than your mom;
My mom's older than yours.
She takes smelly baths; she hides the gray hairs.

My mom's older than yours.
CHORUS
Nyaa nyaa na na na. Nyaa.

OH WHERE, OH WHERE HAS MY LITTLE DOG GONE?

Oh where, oh where has my little dog gone?
Oh where, oh where can he be?
With his ears cut short and his tail cut long,
Oh where, oh where can he be?

THE FOX

The fox went out in the chilly night;
He prayed for the moon to give him light.
He'd many a mile to go that night
Before he reached the town-o, town-o, town-o;
He'd many a mile to go that night
Before he reached the town-o.

He ran till he came to a great big bin;
The ducks and the geese were kept therein.
"A couple of you will grease my chin
Before I leave this town-o, town-o, town-o;
A couple of you will grease my chin
Before I leave this town-o."

So he grabbed a gray goose by the neck
And threw a duck across his back. He didn't mind
Their quack quack quack
And their legs all dangling down-o, down-o, down-o;
He didn't mind their quack quack quack
And their legs all dangling down-o.

Then old Mother Flipper-Flopper jumped out of bed,
And out of the window she stuck her head;
Said, "Get up, John, the gray goose is gone,
And the fox is in the town-o, town-o, town-o";
Said, "Get up, John, the gray goose is gone,
And the fox is in the town-o."

So John, he ran to the top of the hill,
And he blew his horn both loud and shrill.
The fox he said, "I better flee with my kill,
Or they'll soon be on my trail-o, trail-o, trail-o";
The fox he said, "I better flee with my kill,
Or they'll soon be on my trail-o."

He ran till he came to his cozy den,
And there were his little ones, eight, nine and ten.
They said, "Daddy, you better go back again,
'Cause it must be a mighty fine town-o, town-o, town-o";

They said, "Daddy, you better go back again,
'Cause it must be a mighty fine town-o."

So the fox and his wife without any strife,
They cut up the goose with a fork and a knife.
They never had such a supper in their lives,
And the little ones chewed on the bones-o, bones-o,
   bones-o;
They never had such a supper in their lives,
And the little ones chewed on the bones-o.

THE ANIMAL FAIR

I went to the animal fair;
The birds and the beasts were there.
The big baboon by the light of the moon
Was combing his auburn hair.
You ought to have seen the monk;
He jumped on the elephant's trunk.
The elephant sneezed and fell on his knees,
And what became of the monk?

GOING TO THE ZOO
Words and Music by Tom Paxton

Daddy's taking us to the zoo tomorrow,
Zoo tomorrow, zoo tomorrow.
Daddy's taking us to the zoo tomorrow;
We can stay all day.

CHORUS
We're going to the zoo, zoo, zoo.
How about you, you, you?
You can come too, too, too.
We're going to the zoo, zoo, zoo.

See the elephant with the long trunk swingin',
Great big ears and long trunk swingin',
Sniffin' up peanuts with the long trunk swingin'.
We can stay all day.
CHORUS

See all the monkeys scritch scritch scratchin',
Jumpin' all around and scritch scritch scratchin',
Hangin' by their long tails scritch scritch scratchin'.
We can stay all day.
CHORUS

Big black bear all huff huff a-puffin';
Coat's too heavy, he's huff huff a-puffin'.
Don't get too near the huff huff a-puffin',
Or you won't stay all day.
CHORUS

Seals in the pool all honk honk honkin',
Catchin' fish and honk honk honkin',
Little seals honk honk honkin' *(high-pitched voice)*.
We can stay all day.
CHORUS

We stayed all day and we're gettin' sleepy,
Sittin' in the car gettin' sleep sleep sleepy.
Home already and we're sleep sleep sleepy.
We have stayed all day.
We've been to the zoo, zoo, zoo.
So have you, you, you.
You came too, too, too.
We've been to the zoo, zoo, zoo.

Momma's taking us to the zoo tomorrow,
Zoo tomorrow, zoo tomorrow.
Momma's taking us to the zoo tomorrow;
We can stay all day.
CHORUS

THE LITTLE WHITE DUCK
Words by Walt Barrows; Music by Bernard Zaritzky

There's a little white duck *(quack)*
Sitting in the water,
A little white duck *(quack)*
Doing what he oughter.
He took a bite of a lily pad,
Flapped his wings and he said,
"I'm glad I'm a little white duck
Sitting in the water."
Quack, quack, quack.

There's a little green frog *(ribbet)*
Swimming in the water,
A little green frog *(ribbet)*
Doing what he oughter.
He jumped right off of the lily pad
That the little duck bit and he said,
"I'm glad I'm a little green frog
Swimming in the water."
Glumph, glumph, glumph.

There's a little black bug *(chirp)*
Floating on the water,
A little black bug *(chirp)*
Doing what he oughter.
He tickled the frog on the lily pad
That the little duck bit and he said,
"I'm glad I'm a little black bug

13

(continued on next page)

Floating on the water."
Chirp, chirp, chirp.

There's a little red snake *(sss)*
Lying in the water,
A little red snake *(sss)*
Doing what he oughter.
He frightened the duck and the frog so bad;
He ate the little bug and he said,
"I'm glad I'm a little red snake
Lying in the water."
Sss, sss, sss.

Now there's nobody left *(sob)*
Sitting in the water,
Nobody left *(sob)*
Doing what he oughter.
There's nothing left but the lily pad;
The duck and the frog ran away.
It's sad that there's nobody left
Sitting in the water.
Boo, hoo, hoo.

ME AND MY TEDDY BEAR

Words by Jack Winters; Music by J. Fred Coots

In the house next door to me,
A little boy lives there.
At Christmastime, dear Santa Claus
Brought him a teddy bear.
He loves his little teddy bear;
He's with it all day long.
And the sweetest thing you've ever heard
Is to hear him sing this song.
Me and my teddy bear
Have no worries, have no care.
Me and my teddy bear
Just play and play all day.
I love my teddy bear;
He's got one eye and got no hair,
But I love my teddy bear;
We play and play all day.
Ev'ry night he's with me
When I climb up the stairs,
And by my bed he listens
Until I say my prayers.
Oh, me and my teddy bear
Have no worries, have no care.
Me and my teddy bear
Just play and play all day.

OLD MAC DONALD HAD A FARM

Old MacDonald had a farm,
E-I-E-I-O,
And on his farm he had a cow,
E-I-E-I-O.
With a moo-moo here and a moo-moo there,
Here a moo, there a moo, ev'rywhere a moo-moo.
Old MacDonald had a farm,
E-I-E-I-O.

Old MacDonald had a farm,
E-I-E-I-O,
And on his farm he had a pig,
E-I-E-I-O.
With an oink-oink here and an oink-oink there,
Here an oink, there an oink, ev'rywhere an oink-oink.
Old MacDonald had a farm,
E-I-E-I-O.

Old MacDonald had a farm,
E-I-E-I-O,
And on his farm he had a duck,
E-I-E-I-O.
With a quack-quack here and a quack-quack there,
Here a quack, there a quack, ev'rywhere a quack-quack.
Old MacDonald had a farm,
E-I-E-I-O.

Old MacDonald had a farm,
E-I-E-I-O,
And on his farm he had a horse,
E-I-E-I-O.
With a neigh-neigh here and a neigh-neigh there,
Here a neigh, there a neigh, ev'rywhere a neigh-neigh.
Old MacDonald had a farm,
E-I-E-I-O.

Old MacDonald had a farm,
E-I-E-I-O,
And on his farm he had a donkey,
E-I-E-I-O.
With a hee-haw here and a hee-haw there,
Here a hee, there a hee, ev'rywhere a hee-haw.
Old MacDonald had a farm,
E-I-E-I-O.

Old MacDonald had a farm,
E-I-E-I-O,
And on his farm he had some chickens,
E-I-E-I-O.
With a chick-chick here and a chick-chick there,
Here a chick, there a chick, ev'rywhere a chick-chick.

Old MacDonald had a farm,
E-I-E-I-O.

For additional verses, add your own animals.

THE TEDDY BEARS' PICNIC
Words by Jimmy Kennedy; Music by John W. Bratton

If you go down in the woods today,
You're sure of a big surprise.
If you go down in the woods today,
You'd better go in disguise,
For ev'ry bear that ever there was
Will gather there for certain because
Today's the day the teddy bears have their picnic.
Picnic time for teddy bears,
The little teddy bears are having a lovely time today.
Watch them, catch them unawares
And see them picnic on their holiday.
See them gaily gad about;
They love to play and shout;
They never have any care.
At six o'clock their mummies and daddies will take them
　home to bed,
Because they're tired little teddy bears.

I LOVE LITTLE PUSSY

I love little pussy,
Her coat is so warm,
And if I don't hurt her,
She'll do me no harm.
I'll sit by the fire
And give her some food,
And pussy will love me
Because I am good.

I love little pussy,
Her coat is so warm,
And if I don't hurt her,
She'll do me no harm.
I'll not pull her tail
Nor drive her away.
Little pussy and I
Very gently will play.

WILLIE THE WHISTLING GIRAFFE
Words by Rube Goldberg; Music by Ruth Cleary Patterson

The tall giraffe whose neck is long
Can see for miles around,
But the poor thing has no vocal cords,
So he cannot make a sound.

Willie, the baby giraffe,
Felt sad and he just couldn't laugh.
He kept trying to shout,
But nothing came out,
Poor Willie, the baby giraffe.
Willie, the baby giraffe,
He doubled himself near in half.
When he wanted to sing,
Not a note could he bring
From his throat, poor baby giraffe.
But he swallowed a whistle one day,
Which soon made him happy and gay.
When he'd hide in the thistle and whistle and whistle,
The animals all would obey.
Now he's Willie, the whistling giraffe;
We can all hear him whistle and laugh.
All the animals too
Call him King of the Zoo,
King Willie, the whistling giraffe.

PUSSY-CAT, PUSSY-CAT

Pussy-cat, pussy-cat,
Where have you been?
"I've been to London to visit the Queen."
Pussy-cat, pussy-cat,
What did you there?
"I frightened a little mouse under her chair."

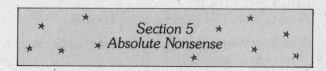

Section 5
Absolute Nonsense

I'M A LITTLE TEAPOT

I'm a little teapot, short and stout.
Here is my handle; here is my spout.
When I get all steamed up, then I shout,
"Tip me over and pour me out."

I'm a very special pot, it's true;
Here, let me show you what it can do.
I can change my handle and my spout;
Tip me over and pour me out.

A-TISKET A-TASKET
Words and Music by Ella Fitzgerald and Van Alexander

A-tisket a-tasket,
A green-and-yellow basket,
I bought a basket for my mommie,

(continued on next page)

On the way I dropped it.
I dropped it, I dropped it,
Yes, on the way I dropped it;
A little girlie picked it up
And took it to the market.
She was truckin' on down the avenue,
Without a single thing to do.
She was peck, peck, peckin' all around,
When she spied it on the ground.
A-tisket a-tasket,
She took my yellow basket,
And if she doesn't bring it back,
I think that I shall die.
(Was it red?)
No, no, no, no.
(Was it brown?)
No, no, no, no.
(Was it blue?)
No, no, no, no.
Just a little yellow basket.

CHICKERY CHICK
Words by Sylvia Dee; Music by Sidney Lippman

Once there lived a chicken who would say "chick-chick,"
"Chick-chick" all day.
Soon that chick got sick and tired of just "chick-chick,"
So one morning he started to say:

CHORUS
"Chickery chick, cha-la, cha-la,
Check-a-la romey in a bananika,
Bollika, wollika, can't you see
Chickery chick is me?"

Ev'ry time you're sick and tired of just the same old thing,
Sayin' just the same old words all day,
Be just like the chicken who found something new to
   sing;
Open up your mouth and start to say,
Oh!
CHORUS

DOWN BY THE STATION
Words and Music by Lee Ricks and Slim Gaillard

This is for the people who never rode the train,
Whether in California or even up in Maine.
Makes no diff'rence if you're two or a hundred and two,
You'll get a treat when you order a seat on the ole choo-
   choo.
Down by the station early in the morning,
See the little puffer bellies all in a row.
See the stationmaster turn the little handle,
Chug, chug, toot, toot,
Off we go.

THE MARVELOUS TOY
Words and Music by Tom Paxton

When I was just a wee little lad
Full of health and joy,
My father homeward came one night
And gave to me a toy.
A wonder to behold it was,
With many colors bright,
And the moment I laid eyes on it,
It became my heart's delight.

CHORUS
It went "zip" when it moved
And "bop" when it stopped
And "whirr" when it stood still.
I never knew just what it was,
And I guess I never will.

The first time that I picked it up,
I had a big surprise,
For right on its bottom were two big buttons
That looked like big green eyes.
I first pushed one and then the other,
And then I twisted its lid,
And when I set it down again,
Here is what it did.
CHORUS

It first marched left and then marched right,
And then marched under a chair,
And when I looked where it had gone,
It wasn't even there!
I started to sob and my daddy laughed,
For he knew that I would find,
When I turned around my marvelous toy
Chuggin' from behind.
CHORUS

Well, the years have gone by too quickly it seems,
And I have my own little boy,
And yesterday I gave to him
My marv'lous little toy.
His eyes nearly popped right out of his head,
And he gave a squeal of glee.
Neither one of us knows just what it is,
But he loves it just like me.
It still goes "zip" when it moves
And "bop" when it stops
And "whirr" when it stands still.
I never knew just what it was,
And I guess I never will.

CEMENT MIXER (PUT-TI, PUT-TI)
Words and Music by Slim Gaillard and Lee Ricks

Cement mixer! put-ti, put-ti,
Cement mixer! put-ti, put-ti,
Cement mixer! put-ti, put-ti,
A puddle o' vooty, puddle o' gooty, puddle o' scooty.
Cement mixer! put-ti, put-ti,
Cement mixer! put-ti, put-ti,
Cement mixer! put-ti, put-ti,
A puddle o' veet,
Concrete.
First you get some gravel,
Pour it in a vout;
To mix a mess o' mortar, you add cement and water.
See the mellow roony come out, slurp, slurp, slurp.
Cement mixer! put-ti, put-ti,
Cement mixer! put-ti, put-ti,
Cement mixer! put-ti, put-ti,
Who wants a bucket of cement?

BINGO

There was a farmer who had a dog,
And Bingo was his name-o.
B-I-N-G-O, B-I-N-G-O, B-I-N-G-O,
And Bingo was his name-o.

I KNOW AN OLD LADY
Words and Music by Alan Mills and Rose Bonne

I know an old lady who swallowed a fly.
I don't know why she swallowed a fly!
I guess she'll die!

I know an old lady who swallowed a spider
That wriggled and wriggled and tickled inside her.
She swallowed a spider to catch the fly,
But I don't know why she swallowed the fly.
I guess she'll die!

I know an old lady who swallowed a bird!
Now, how absurd to swallow a bird!
She swallowed the bird to catch the spider
That wriggled and wriggled and tickled inside her.
She swallowed the spider to catch the fly,
But I don't know why she swallowed the fly.
I guess she'll die!

I know an old lady who swallowed a cat!
Now, fancy that to swallow a cat!
She swallowed the cat to catch the bird.
She swallowed the bird to catch the spider
That wriggled and wriggled and tickled inside her.
She swallowed the spider to catch the fly,
But I don't know why she swallowed the fly.
I guess she'll die!

I know an old lady who swallowed a dog!
My, what a hog to swallow a dog!
She swallowed the dog to catch the cat.
She swallowed the cat to catch the bird.
She swallowed the bird to catch the spider
That wriggled and wriggled and tickled inside her.
She swallowed the spider to catch the fly,
But I don't know why she swallowed the fly.
I guess she'll die!

I know an old lady who swallowed a goat!
Just opened her throat and in walked the goat!
She swallowed the goat to catch the dog.
She swallowed the dog to catch the cat.
She swallowed the cat to catch the bird.
She swallowed the bird to catch the spider
That wriggled and wriggled and tickled inside her.
She swallowed the spider to catch the fly,
But I don't know why she swallowed the fly.
I guess she'll die!

I know an old lady who swallowed a cow!
I don't know how she swallowed a cow!
She swallowed the cow to catch the goat.
She swallowed the goat to catch the dog.
She swallowed the dog to catch the cat.
She swallowed the cat to catch the bird.
She swallowed the bird to catch the spider
That wriggled and wriggled and tickled inside her.
She swallowed the spider to catch the fly,
But I don't know why she swallowed the fly.
I guess she'll die!

(continued on next page)

I know an old lady who swallowed a horse.
(spoken) She's dead, of course!

ON TOP OF SPAGHETTI
Words and Music by Tom Glazer

On top of spaghetti
All covered with cheese,
I lost my poor meatball
When somebody sneezed.
It rolled off the table
And onto the floor,
And then my poor meatball
Rolled out of the door.
It rolled in the garden
And under a bush,
And then my poor meatball
Was nothing but mush.
The mush was as tasty
As tasty could be,
And early next summer,
It grew into a tree.
The tree was all covered
With beautiful moss;
It grew lovely meatballs
And tomato sauce.
So if you eat spaghetti
All covered with cheese,
Hold on to your meatballs
And don't ever sneeze.
A-choo!

MAIL MYSELF TO YOU
Words and Music by Woody Guthrie

I'm a-gonna wrap myself in paper;
I'm gonna daub myself with glue,
Stick some stamps on top of my head,
I'm gonna mail myself to you.
I'm a-gonna tie me up in a red string;
I'm gonna tie blue ribbons too.
I'm a-gonna climb up in my mailbox;
I'm gonna mail myself to you.
When you see me in your mailbox,
Cut the string and let me out.
Wash the glue off my fingers;
Stick some bubble gum in my mouth.
Take me out of my wrapping paper;
Wash the stamps off my head.
Pour me full of ice-cream sodies;

Put me in my nice warm bed.

PUT YOUR FINGER IN THE AIR
Words and Music by Woody Guthrie

Put your finger in the air, in the air; *(in the air)*
Put your finger in the air, in the air; *(in the air)*
Put your finger in the air
And leave it about a year;
Put your finger in the air, in the air. *(in the air)*

Put your finger on your head, on your head; *(on your head)*
Put your finger on your head, on your head; *(on your head)*
Put your finger on your head;
Tell me is it green or red;
Put your finger on your head, on your head. *(on your head)*

Put your finger on your nose, on your nose; *(on your nose)*
Put your finger on your nose, on your nose; *(on your nose)*
Put your finger on your nose
And feel the cold wind blow;
Put your finger on your nose, on your nose. *(on your nose)*

JOHN JACOB JINGLEHEIMER SCHMIDT

John Jacob Jingleheimer Schmidt,
His name is my name too.
Whenever we go out
And people always shout,
"John Jacob Jingleheimer Schmidt."
Dah dah dah dah,
Dah dah dah.

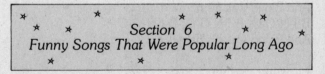

Section 6
Funny Songs That Were Popular Long Ago

BARNEY GOOGLE
Words and Music by Billy Rose and Con Conrad

Who's the most important man this country ever knew?
Who's the man our presidents tell all their troubles to?
No, it isn't Mister Bryan

And it isn't Mister Hughes;
I'm mighty proud that I'm allowed a chance to introduce
Barney Google with his goo-goo-googly eyes.
Barney Google had a wife three times his size.
She sued Barney for divorce;
Now he's living with his horse.
Barney Google with his goo-goo-googly eyes.

Who's the greatest lover that this country ever knew?
Who's the man that Valentino takes his hat off to?
No, it isn't Douglas Fairbanks
That the ladies rave about,
When he arrives who makes the wives chase all their
    husbands out.
Barney Google with his goo-goo-googly eyes.
Barney Google bet his horse would win the prize.
When the horses ran that day,
Spark Plug ran the other way.
Barney Google with his goo-goo-googly eyes.

MAIRZY DOATS
Words and Music by Milton Drake, Al Hoffman and
Jerry Livingston

Mairzy doats and dozy doats and liddle lamzy divey,
A kiddley divey too, wouldn't you?
Yes! mairzy doats and dozy doats and liddle lamzy divey,
A kiddley divey too, wouldn't you?
If the words sound queer and funny to your ear,
A little bit jumbled and jivey,
Sing "Mares eat oats and does eat oats,
And little lambs eat ivy."
Oh! mairzy doats and dozy doats and liddle lamzy divey,
A kiddley divey too, wouldn't you?
A kiddley divey too, wouldn't you?

THE FLAT FOOT FLOOGEE
Words and Music by Slim Gaillard, Slam Stewart and
Bud Green

The flat foot floogee with the floy floy,
The flat foot floogee with the floy floy,
The flat foot floogee with the floy floy,
Floy doy, floy doy, floy doy, floy doy.
The flat foot floogee with the flou (rhymes with "how")
    flou,
The flat foot floogee with the flou flou,
The flat foot floogee with the flou flou,
Flou dow, flou dow, flou dow, flow dow.

If you're feelin' low-down,
Don't know what to do,
And you want a showdown,
Here's the only dance for you.
The flat foot floogee with the floy floy,
The flat foot floogee with the floy floy,
The flat foot floogee with the floy floy,
Floy doy, floy doy, floy doy, floy doy.

(I SCREAM—YOU SCREAM—WE ALL SCREAM FOR) ICE CREAM
Words and Music by Howard Johnson, Billy Moll
and Robert King

I scream, you scream,
We all scream for ice cream,
Rah, rah, rah!
Tuesdays, Mondays,
We all scream for sundaes,
Siss, boom, bah!
Boola, boola,
Sasparoola,
If you've got chocolet,
We'll take vanoola.
I scream, you scream,
We all scream for ice cream.
Rah, rah, rah!

I scream, you scream,
We all scream for ice cream,
Rah, rah, rah!
Frosted malted
Or peppered and salted,
Siss, boom, bah!
Oh, spumoni,
Oh, tortoni
And, confidentially,
Oh, oh, baloney.
I scream, you scream,
We all scream for ice cream,
Rah, rah, rah!

THE HUT-SUT SONG
Words and Music by Leo V. Killion, Ted McMichael
and Jack Owens

Hut-sut Rawlson on the rillerah
And a brawla, brawla soo-it,
Hut-sut Rawlson on the rillerah
And a brawla soo-it, .

(continued on next page)

Hut-sut Rawlson on the rillerah
And a brawla, brawla soo-it,
Hut-sut Rawlson on the rillerah
And a brawla soo-it.
Now the Rawlson is a Swedish town;
The rillerah is a stream.
The brawla is the boy and girl;
The hut-sut is their dream.
Hut-sut Rawlson on the rillerah
And a brawla, brawla soo-it,
Hut-sut Rawlson on the rillerah
And a brawla soo-it.

IT AIN'T GONNA RAIN NO MORE
New version by Bill Lewis

Oh, it ain't gonna rain no more, no more;
It ain't gonna rain no more.
Ain't gonna snow and it ain't gonna pour,
Oh, it ain't gonna rain no more.

Oh, it ain't gonna rain no more, no more;
It ain't gonna rain no more.
How in the heck can I wash my neck
When it ain't gonna rain no more?

Oh, I had a cat and I named him Tom,
Let him out one day.
A big dog chased him down the street,
And Tom-cat ran away.

Now Tom came back big and fat,
How that cat did purr.
Now how on earth could Tom give birth;
I guess that "he's" a "her"!

Oh, it ain't gonna rain no more, no more;
It ain't gonna rain no more.
How in the dickens can I count my chickens
If it ain't gonna rain no more?

Made a garden on my roof,
Weeded every day.
Prayed for rain, but when it came,
It washed my roof away.

It ain't gonna rain no more, no more;
It ain't gonna rain no more.
Now I s'pose I can pick my rose;
It ain't gonna rain no more.

Oh, it isn't going to rain anymore, anymore;
It isn't going to rain anymore.
The grammar's right, but it sure sounds trite,

And what's more it's a bore.

Oh, it ain't gonna rain no more, no more;
It ain't gonna rain no more.
How in the deuce can I cook my goose
If it ain't gonna rain no more?

Oh, I like to sing this silly song,
Make up verses too.
It's no offense if they don't make sense;
I can, why can't you?

CAMPTOWN RACES
Words and Music by Stephen Foster

The Camptown ladies sing this song,
Doo-dah, doo-dah!
The Camptown racetrack's five miles long,
Oh, doo-dah day!
I come down there with my hat caved in,
Doo-dah, doo-dah!
I go back home with a pocket full of tin,
Oh, doo-dah day!

CHORUS
Goin' to run all night,
Goin' to run all day.
I'll bet my money on a bobtail nag;
Somebody bet on the bay.

The long-tail filly and the big black horse,
Doo-dah, doo-dah!
They fly the track and they both cut across,
Oh, doo-dah day!
The blind horse stickin' in a big mudhole,
Doo-dah, doo-dah!
Can't touch bottom with a ten-foot pole,
Oh, doo-dah day!
CHORUS

FATHER'S OLD GREY WHISKERS

I have a dear old daddy
For whom I nightly pray.
He has a set of whiskers
That are always in the way.

CHORUS
They're always in the way;
The cow eats them for hay.
They hide the dirt on Daddy's shirt;
They're always in the way.

Around the supper table,
We make a happy group,

Until dear father's whiskers
Get tangled in the soup.
CHORUS

Father had a strong back;
Now it's all caved in.
He stepped upon his whiskers
And walked up to his chin.
CHORUS

We have a dear old mother;
With him at night she sleeps.
She wakes up in the morning
Eating shredded wheat.
CHORUS

We have a dear old brother;
He has a Ford machine.
He uses Father's whiskers
To strain the gasoline.
CHORUS

Father fought in World War II;
He wasn't killed, you see.
He hid behind his whiskers
And fooled the enemy.
CHORUS

Father in a tavern,
He likes his lager beer.
He pins a pretzel on his nose
To keep his whiskers clear.
CHORUS

THREE LITTLE FISHIES (ITTY BITTY POO)
Words and Music by Saxie Dowell

Down in de meddy in a itty bitty poo
Fam fee itty fitty and a mama fitty foo.
"Fim," fed de mama fitty,
"Fim if oo tan."
And dey fam and dey fam all over de dam.
Boop boop dit-tem dat-tem what-tem Chu!
Boop boop dit-tem dat-tem what-tem Chu!
Boop boop dit-tem dat-tem what-tem Chu!
And dey fam and dey fam all over de dam.

Down in the meadow in a little bitty pool
Swam three little fishies and a mama fishie too.
"Swim," said the mama fishie,
"Swim if you can."
And they swam and they swam all over the dam.
Boop boop dit-tem dat-tem what-tem Chu!
Boop boop dit-tem dat-tem what-tem Chu!
Boop boop dit-tem dat-tem what-tem Chu!

And they swam and they swam all over the dam.

"Top!" ted de mama fitty, "or oo ill det ost."
De fee itty fitty dinna anna be bossed.
De fee itty fitty ent off on a spwee,
And dey fam and dey fam ite out to de fee.
Boop boop dit-tem dat-tem what-tem Chu!
Boop boop dit-tem dat-tem what-tem Chu!
Boop boop dit-tem dat-tem what-tem Chu!
And dey fam and dey fam ite out to de fee.

"Stop," said the mama fishie, "or you will get lost."
The three little fishies didn't wanna be bossed.
The three little fishies went off on a spree,
And they swam and they swam right out to the sea.
Boop boop dit-tem dat-tem what-tem Chu!
Boop boop dit-tem dat-tem what-tem Chu!
Boop boop dit-tem dat-tem what-tem Chu!
And they swam and they swam right out to the sea.

"Whee!" elled de itty fitties, "Ears a wot of fun,
Ee'll fim in de fee ill de day is un."
Dey fam and dey fam, and it was a wark,
Till aw of a tudden dey taw a tark!
Boop boop dit-tem dat-tem what-tem Chu!
Boop boop dit-tem dat-tem what-tem Chu!
Boop boop dit-tem dat-tem what-tem Chu!
Till aw of a tudden dey taw a tark!

"Whee!" yelled the little fishies, "Here's a lot of fun.
We'll swim in the sea till the day is done."
They swam and they swam, and it was a lark,
Till all of a sudden they saw a shark!
Boop boop dit-tem dat-tem what-tem Chu!
Boop boop dit-tem dat-tem what-tem Chu!
Boop boop dit-tem dat-tem what-tem Chu!
Till all of a sudden they saw a shark!

"He'p!" tied de itty fitties, "Dee! ook at all de fales!"
And twit as dey tood, dey turned on deir tails!
And bat to de poo in de meddy dey fam,
And dey fam and dey fam bat over de dam.
Boop boop dit-tem dat-tem what-tem Chu!
Boop boop dit-tem dat-tem what-tem Chu!
Boop boop dit-tem dat-tem what-tem Chu!
And dey fam and dey fam bat over de dam.

"Help!" cried the little fishies, "Gee! look at all the
*   whales!"*
And quick as they could, they turned on their tails.
And back to the pool in the meadow they swam,
And they swam and they swam back over the dam.
Boop boop dit-tem dat-tem what-tem Chu!
Boop boop dit-tem dat-tem what-tem Chu!
Boop boop dit-tem dat-tem what-tem Chu!

(continued on next page)

And they swam and they swam back over the dam.

M-I-S-S-I-S-S-I-P-P-I

Words by Bert Hanlon and Benny Ryan;
Music by Harry Tierney

M-i-s-s-i-s-s-i-p-p-i,
That used to be so hard to spell,
It used to make me cry.
But since I studied spelling,
It's just like pumpkin pie,
M-i-s-s-i-s-s-i-p-p-i.

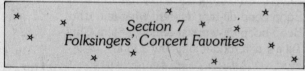

Section 7
Folksingers' Concert Favorites

I'VE BEEN WORKING ON THE RAILROAD

I've been working on the railroad
All the livelong day.
I've been working on the railroad
To pass the time of day.
Don't you hear the whistle blowing?
Rise up so early in the morn.
Don't you hear the captain shouting,
"Dinah, blow your horn"?
Dinah, won't you blow,
Dinah, won't you blow,
Dinah, won't you blow your horn?
Dinah, won't you blow,
Dinah, won't you blow,
Dinah, won't you blow your horn?
Someone's in the kitchen with Dinah;
Someone's in the kitchen I know.
Someone's in the kitchen with Dinah,
Strumming on the old banjo.
Fee-fi, fiddle-e-i-o,
Fee-fi, fiddle-e-i-o,
Fee-fi, fiddle-e-i-o,
Strumming on the old banjo.

PUFF (THE MAGIC DRAGON)

Words and Music by Peter Yarrow and Leonard Lipton

Puff, the magic dragon, lived by the sea
And frolicked in the autumn mist in a land called
    Honah-Lee.
Little Jackie Paper loved that rascal Puff
And brought him strings and sealing wax and other fancy
    stuff.

CHORUS
Oh! Puff, the magic dragon, lived by the sea
And frolicked in the autumn mist in a land called Honah-
    Lee.
Puff, the magic dragon, lived by the sea
And frolicked in the autumn mist in a land called Honah-
    Lee.

Together they would travel on a boat with billowed sail;
Jackie kept a lookout perched on Puff's gigantic tail.
Noble kings and princes would bow whene'er they
    came;
Pirate ships would low'r their flag when Puff roared out
    his name.
CHORUS

A dragon lives forever but not so little boys;
Painted wings and giant rings make way for other toys.
One grey night it happened, Jackie Paper came no more,
And Puff that mighty dragon, he ceased his fearless roar.
CHORUS

His head was bent in sorrow; green scales fell like rain.
Puff no longer went to play along the cherry lane.
Without his lifelong friend, Puff could not be brave,
So Puff that mighty dragon sadly slipped into his cave.
CHORUS

CLEMENTINE

In a cavern, in a canyon,
Excavating for a mine,
Dwelt a miner, forty-niner,
And his daughter Clementine.

CHORUS
Oh, my darling,
Oh, my darling,
Oh, my darling Clementine,
You are lost and gone forever,
Dreadful sorry, Clementine.

Light she was and like a fairy,
And her shoes were number nine,

Herring boxes without topses,
Sandals were for Clementine.
CHORUS

Drove she ducklings to the water
Ev'ry morning just at nine,
Hit her foot against a splinter,
Fell into the foaming brine.
CHORUS

Ruby lips above the water
Blowing bubbles soft and fine,
But, alas, I was no swimmer,
So I lost my Clementine.
CHORUS

LITTLE BROWN JUG

My wife and I lived all alone
In a little log hut we called our own.
She loved gin and I loved rum;
I tell you what we'd lots of fun.

CHORUS
Ha ha ha,
You and me,
Little brown jug don't I love thee.
Ha ha ha,
You and me,
Little brown jug don't I love thee.

'Tis you who makes my friends and foes;
'Tis you who makes me wear old clothes.
Here you are so near my nose,
So tip her up and down she goes.
CHORUS

HA, HA, THIS-A-WAY
Words and Music by Huddie Ledbetter;
Collected and adapted by John A. Lomax and Alan Lomax

CHORUS
Ha, ha, this-a-way,
Ha, ha, that-a-way,
Ha, ha, this-a-way,
Then, oh, then.
Hi, this-a-way,
Hi, that-a-way,
Hi, this-a-way,
Then, oh, then.

When I was a little boy, little boy, little boy,
When I was a little boy twelve years old,
Papa went an' left me, left me, left me;

Papa went an' left me to save my soul.
CHORUS

Momma came an' got me, got me, got me;
Momma came an' got me to save my soul.
Momma didn't whiff me or whip me, whiff me;
Momma didn't whiff me, so I was tol'.
CHORUS

Papa drank whiskey, whiskey, whiskey;
Papa drank whiskey, so I was tol'.
Momma was frisky, frisky, frisky;
Momma was frisky, so I was tol'.
CHORUS

I went to school, went to school, went to school, boys,
I went to school when I was twelve years old.
Obeyed the rules, the rules, the rules, boys,
Obeyed the rules as I was told.
CHORUS

Learned my lesson, lesson, lesson,
Learned my lesson as I was tol'.
Wasn't that a blessin', blessin', blessin'?
Wasn't that a blessin' to save my soul?
CHORUS

Liked my teacher, teacher, teacher,
Liked my teacher, so I was tol'.
Prayed like a preacher, preacher, preacher,
Prayed like a preacher to save my soul.
CHORUS

I went to school, went to school, went to school;
I went to school when I was twelve years old.
Teacher didn't whiff me, whiff me, whiff me;
Teacher didn't whiff me to save my soul.
CHORUS

THE GREY GOOSE
Words and Music by Huddie Ledbetter;
Collected and adapted by John A. Lomax and Alan Lomax

Preacher went a-huntin',
Lord, Lord, Lord.
Preacher went a-huntin',
Lord, Lord, Lord.
Carried 'long his shotgun,
Lord, Lord, Lord.
Carried 'long his shotgun,
Lord, Lord, Lord.
'Long came a grey goose,
Lord, Lord, Lord.

(continued on next page)

'Long came a grey goose,
Lord, Lord, Lord.
Gun went a-boo-loo,
Lord, Lord, Lord.
Gun went a-boo-loo,
Lord, Lord, Lord.
Down came a grey goose,
Lord, Lord, Lord.
Down came a grey goose,
Lord, Lord, Lord.
He was six weeks a-fallin',
Lord, Lord, Lord.
He was six weeks a-fallin',
Lord, Lord, Lord.
Then they gave a feather-pickin',
Lord, Lord, Lord.
Then they gave a feather-pickin',
Lord, Lord, Lord.
Your wife an' my wife,
Lord, Lord, Lord.
Your wife an' my wife,
Lord, Lord, Lord.
They was six weeks a-pickin',
Lord, Lord, Lord.
They was six weeks a-pickin',
Lord, Lord, Lord.
Great God, great God,
Lord, Lord, Lord.
Great God, great God,
Lord, Lord, Lord.
Well, I wonder what's the matter,
Lord, Lord, Lord.
Well, I wonder what's the matter,
Lord, Lord, Lord.
So they put him on to parboil,
Lord, Lord, Lord.
So they put him on to parboil,
Lord, Lord, Lord.
He was six weeks a-boilin',
Lord, Lord, Lord.
He was six weeks a-boilin',
Lord, Lord, Lord.
So they put him on the table,
Lord, Lord, Lord.
So they put him on the table,
Lord, Lord, Lord.
Fork couldn't stick him,
Lord, Lord, Lord.
Fork couldn't stick him,
Lord, Lord, Lord.
Knife couldn't cut him,

Lord, Lord, Lord.
Knife couldn't cut him,
Lord, Lord, Lord.
Great God, it's a grey goose,
Lord, Lord, Lord.
Great God, it's a grey goose,
Lord, Lord, Lord.
So they took him to the hog pen,
Lord, Lord, Lord.
So they took him to the hog pen,
Lord, Lord, Lord.
Broke the sow's teeth out,
Lord, Lord, Lord.
Broke the sow's teeth out,
Lord, Lord, Lord.
Great God, it's a grey goose,
Lord, Lord, Lord.
Great God, it's a grey goose,
Lord, Lord, Lord.

ROCK ISLAND LINE
Words and Music by Paul Campbell and Joel Newman

CHORUS
Oh, the Rock Island Line, it is a mighty good road.
Oh, the Rock Island Line is the road to ride.
The Rock Island Line, it is a mighty good road.
Well, if you want to ride, you got to ride it like you find it.
Get your ticket at the station for the Rock Island Line.

It's cloudy in the west, looks like rain.
Bought me a ticket on a railroad train.
Pour on the water; shovel on the coal;
Stick your head out the window; see the drivers roll.
CHORUS

The seven forty-five was always late,
But arrived today at a quarter to eight.
The engineer said when they cheered his name,
"We're right on time, but this is yesterday's train."
CHORUS

The engineer said before he died,
"There's two more drinks that I would like to try."
The conductor said, "What can they be?"
"A hot glass of water and a cold cup of tea."
CHORUS

POLLY-WOLLY-DOODLE

Oh, I went down South for to see my gal,
Sing polly-wolly-doodle all the day.
My Sally is a spunky gal,
Sing polly-wolly-doodle all the day.

CHORUS
Fare thee well,
Fare thee well,
Fare thee well, my fairy fay,
For I'm goin' to Lou'siana
For to see my Suzyanna,
Sing polly-wolly-doodle all the day.

Oh, my Sal she is a maiden fair,
Sing polly-wolly-doodle all the day.
With curly eyes and laughing hair,
Sing polly-wolly-doodle all the day.
CHORUS

Oh, a grasshopper sittin' on a railroad track,
Sing polly-wolly-doodle all the day.
A-pickin' his teeth with a carpet tack,
Sing polly-wolly-doodle all the day.
CHORUS

Oh, I went to bed, but it wasn't no use,
Sing polly-wolly-doodle all the day.
My feet stuck out like a chicken roost,
Sing polly-wolly-doodle all the day.
CHORUS

Behind the barn down on my knees,
Sing polly-wolly-doodle all the day.
I thought I heard a chicken sneeze,
Sing polly-wolly-doodle all the day.
CHORUS

He sneezed so hard with the whooping cough,
Sing polly-wolly-doodle all the day.
He sneezed his head and tail right off,
Sing polly-wolly-doodle all the day.
CHORUS

IF YOU'RE HAPPY AND YOU KNOW IT
(CLAP YOUR HANDS)

If you're happy and you know it, clap your hands. *(clap, clap)*
If you're happy and you know it, clap your hands. *(clap, clap)*
If you're happy and you know it,
Then your face will surely show it;
If you're happy and you know it, clap your hands. *(clap, clap)*

If you're happy and you know it, tap your toe. *(tap, tap)*
If you're happy and you know it, tap your toe. *(tap, tap)*
If you're happy and you know it,
Then your face will surely show it;
If you're happy and you know it, tap your toe. *(tap, tap)*

If you're happy and you know it, nod your head. *(nod, nod)*
If you're happy and you know it, nod your head. *(nod, nod)*
If you're happy and you know it,
Then your face will surely show it;
If you're happy and you know it, nod your head. *(nod, nod)*

JOHN BROWN'S BABY

John Brown's baby had a cold upon its chest;
John Brown's baby had a cold upon its chest;
John Brown's baby had a cold upon its chest;
And they rubbed it in with camphorated oil.

SHE'LL BE COMIN' ROUND THE MOUNTAIN
New words by Paul and Dan Fox

She'll be comin' round the mountain when she comes;
She'll be comin' round the mountain when she comes.
She'll be comin' round the mountain;
She'll be comin' round the mountain;
She'll be comin' round the mountain when she comes.

She'll be ridin' on a camel when she comes;
She'll be ridin' on a camel when she comes.
She'll be ridin' on a camel
Or some other mangy mammal;
She'll be ridin' on a camel when she comes.

She'll be tuggin' on two turtles when she comes;
She'll be tuggin' on two turtles when she comes.
She'll be tuggin' on two turtles;
They'll be wearin' purple girdles;
She'll be tuggin' on two turtles when she comes.

She'll be carvin' three thick thistles when she comes;
She'll be carvin' three thick thistles when she comes.
She'll be carvin' three thick thistles
Just to make some penny whistles;
She'll be carvin' three thick thistles when she comes.

She'll be pluckin' four fat pheasants when she comes;
She'll be pluckin' four fat pheasants when she comes.
She'll be pluckin' four fat pheasants
To give as Christmas presents;

(continued on next page)

She'll be pluckin' four fat pheasants when she comes.

She'll be feedin' five fast foxes when she comes;
She'll be feedin' five fast foxes when she comes.
She'll be feedin' five fast foxes,
Eatin' fast food in five boxes;
She'll be feedin' five fast foxes when she comes.

She'll hold six scary spiders when she comes;
She'll hold six scary spiders when she comes.
First, a small one sat beside her,
Then the others tried to bite her;
Now she's holdin' no more spiders when she comes.

She'll send seven stingin' starfish when she comes;
She'll send seven stingin' starfish when she comes.
She'll send seven stingin' starfish;
Did you know that starfish are fish?
She'll send seven stingin' starfish when she comes.

She'll ride eight overweight elephants when she comes;
She'll ride eight overweight elephants when she comes.
She'll ride eight overweight elephants;
How she got 'em is just irrelevance;
She'll ride eight overweight elephants when she comes.

She'll be herdin' nine fine swine when she comes;
She'll be herdin' nine fine swine when she comes.
She'll be herdin' nine fine swine,
Snout to nose in one straight line;
She'll be herdin' nine fine swine when she comes.

She'll be ticklin' ten tan terriers when she comes;
She'll be ticklin' ten tan terriers when she comes.
She'll be ticklin' ten tan terriers;
Come along, the more the merrier;
She'll be ticklin' ten tan terriers when she comes.

Oh, we'll all go down to meet her when she comes;
Oh, we'll all go down to meet her when she comes.
Oh, we'll all go down to meet her;
Oh, we'll all go down to greet her;
Oh, we'll all go down to meet her when she comes.

HUSH, LITTLE BABY

Hush, little baby, don't say a word;
Mama's gonna buy you a mockingbird.
If that mockingbird don't sing,
Mama's gonna buy you a diamond ring.
If that diamond ring gets broke,
Mama's gonna buy you a billy goat.
If that billy goat don't pull,
Mama's gonna buy you a cart 'n' bull.

If that cart 'n' bull turn over,
Mama's gonna buy you a dog named Rover.
If that dog named Rover don't bark,
Mama's gonna buy you a horse 'n' cart.
If that horse 'n' cart fall down,
You'll be the sweetest little baby in town.

A FROG WENT A-COURTIN'

A frog went a-courtin'; he did ride.
H'm, h'm,
H'm, h'm.
A frog went a-courtin'; he did ride
With a sword and a pistol by his side.
H'm, h'm,
H'm, h'm.

He rode up to Miss Mousie's den.
H'm, h'm,
H'm, h'm.
He rode up to Miss Mousie's den,
Said "Please, Miss Mousie, won't you let me in?"
H'm, h'm,
H'm, h'm.

"Yes, Sir Frog, I sit and spin."
H'm, h'm,
H'm, h'm.
"Yes, Sir Frog, I sit and spin;
Pray Mister Froggie, won't you walk in?"
H'm, h'm,
H'm, h'm.

The frog said, "My dear, I've come to see."
H'm, h'm,
H'm, h'm.
The frog said, "My dear, I've come to see
If you, Miss Mousie, will marry me."
H'm, h'm,
H'm, h'm.

"I don't know what to say to that."
H'm, h'm,
H'm, h'm.
"I don't know what to say to that
Till I speak with my Uncle Rat."
H'm, h'm,
H'm, h'm.

When Uncle Rat came riding home.
H'm, h'm,
H'm, h'm.
When Uncle Rat came riding home,
Said he, "Who's been here since I've been gone?"

H'm, h'm,
H'm, h'm.

"A fine young froggie has been here."
H'm, h'm,
H'm, h'm.
"A fine young froggie has been here;
He means to marry me it's clear."
H'm, h'm,
H'm, h'm.

So Uncle Rat, he rode to town.
H'm, h'm,
H'm, h'm.
So Uncle Rat, he rode to town
And bought his niece a wedding gown.
H'm, h'm,
H'm, h'm.

The frog and mouse they went to France.
H'm, h'm,
H'm, h'm.
The frog and mouse they went to France,
And that's the end of my romance.
H'm, h'm,
H'm, h'm.

OLD DAN TUCKER

I come to town the other night;
I heard the noise an' saw the fight.
The watchman was a-runnin' roun',
Cryin' "Old Dan Tucker's come to town."

CHORUS
So get out the way for Old Dan Tucker;
Get out the way for Old Dan Tucker;
Get out the way for Old Dan Tucker;
He's too late to come for supper.

Old Dan, he went down to the mill
To get some meal to put in the swill.
The miller swore by the point of his knife,
He never seen such a man in his life.
CHORUS

Old Dan Tucker, he got drunk;
He fell in the fire and he kicked up a chunk.
A red-hot coal rolled in his shoe,
And good Lord, boys, how the ashes flew.
CHORUS

Old Dan Tucker was a fine old man,
Washed his face in a frying pan,
Combed his hair with a wagon wheel,

Died with a toothache in his heel.
CHORUS

RIDE A COCK-HORSE

Ride a cock-horse to Banbury Cross
To see a fine lady upon a white horse,
Rings on her fingers and bells on her toes;
She shall have music wherever she goes.

POP! GOES THE WEASEL

All around the cobbler's bench,
The monkey chased the weasel.
The monkey thought 'twas all in fun,
Pop goes the weasel.

CHORUS
A penny for a spool of thread,
A penny for a needle.
That's the way the money goes,
Pop goes the weasel.

Rufus has the whooping cough,
And Sally has the measles,
And that's the way the doctor goes,
Pop goes the weasel.
CHORUS

THIS LAND IS YOUR LAND
Words and Music by Woody Guthrie

This land is your land;
This land is my land.
From California to the New York island,
From the redwood forest to the Gulf Stream waters,
This land was made for you and me.

As I was walking that ribbon of highway,
I saw above me that endless skyway;
I saw below me that golden valley.
This land was made for you and me.

I've roamed and rambled, and I followed my footsteps
To the sparkling sands of her diamond deserts,
And all around me a voice was sounding,
This land was made for you and me.

When the sun came shining and I was strolling,
And the wheat fields waving and the dust clouds rolling,
As the fog was lifting, a voice was chanting,
This land was made for you and me.

(continued on next page)

Nobody living can ever stop me
As I go walking that freedom highway.
Nobody living can ever make me turn back;
This land was made for you and me.

BE KIND TO YOUR WEB-FOOTED FRIENDS

Be kind to your web-footed friends,
For a duck may be somebody's mother.
You may think that this is the end,
And it is.

Section 8
Songs Children Sing in Many Countries

MARIANNE

Words and Music by Terry Gilkyson, Richard Dehr and
Frank Miller

Marianne, oh, Marianne, oh, won't you marry me?
We can have a bamboo hut and brandy in the tea.
Leave your fat old mama home; she never will say yes.
If Mama don't know now, she can guess.
(spoken) My, my, yes.

CHORUS
All day, all night, Marianne,
Down by the seaside siftin' sand.
Even little children love Marianne,
Down by the seaside siftin' sand.

When she walks along the shore, people pause to greet.
White birds fly around her; little fish come to her feet.
In her heart is love, but I'm the only mortal man
Who's allowed to kiss my Marianne.
(spoken) Don't rush me.
CHORUS

When we marry, we will have a time you never saw.
I will be so happy, I will kiss my mother-in-law.
(phooey!)
Children by the dozen in and out the bamboo hut,
One for ev'ry palm tree and cokynut.
(spoken) Hurry up now.
CHORUS

ALOUETTE

NOTE: Lines in italics give the pronunciations for the French words.

CHORUS
Oh, Alouette, gentille Alouette;
Alouette, je t'y plumerai.
Alouette, gentille Alouette;
Alouette, je t'y plumerai.

Oh, Ah-loo-et-tuh, zhahn-tee Ah-loo-et-tuh;
Ah-loo-et-tuh, zhe tuh plü-me-ray.
Ah-loo-et-tuh, zhahn-tee Ah-loo-et-tuh;
Ah-loo-et-tuh, zhe tuh plü-me-ray.

Je t'y plumerai la têt';
Je t'y plumerai la têt';
Et la têt', et la têt',
Alouett', Alouett'.

Zhe tuh plü-me-ray la tet;
Zhe tuh plü-me-ray la tet;
Eh la tet, eh la tet,
Ah-loo-et, Ah-loo-et.
CHORUS

Je t'y plumerai le bec;
(Zhe tuh plü-me-ray le bek;)
Je t'y plumerai le bec.
Et le bec, et le bec,
Et la têt', et la têt',
Alouett', Alouett'.
CHORUS

Je t'y plumerai le nez;
(Zhe tuh plü-me-ray le nay;)
Je t'y plumerai le nez.
Et le bec, et le bec,
Et la têt', et la têt',
Alouett', Alouett'.
CHORUS

Je t'y plumerai les yeux;
(Zhe tuh plü-me-ray lay zyœ;)
Je t'y plumerai les yeux.
Et le nez, et le nez,
Et le bec, et le bec,
Et la têt', et la têt',
Alouett', Alouett'.
CHORUS

Je t'y plumerai le cou;
(Zhe tuh plü-me-ray le koo;)
Je t'y plumerai le cou.

Et les yeux, et les yeux,
Et le nez, et le nez,
Et le bec, et le bec,
Et la têt', et la têt',
Alouett', Alouett'.
CHORUS

Je t'y plumerai les ailes;
(Zhe tuh plü-me-ray lay zel;)
Je t'y plumerai les ailes.
Et le cou, et le cou,
Et les yeux, et les yeux,
Et le nez, et le nez,
Et le bec, et le bec,
Et la têt', et la têt',
Alouett', Alouett'.
CHORUS

Je t'y plumerai le dos;
(Zhe tuh plü-me-ray le doh;)
Je t'y plumerai le dos.
Et les ailes, et les ailes,
Et le cou, et le cou,
Et les yeux, et les yeux,
Et le nez, et le nez,
Et le bec, et le bec,
Et la têt', et la têt',
Alouett', Alouett'.
CHORUS

Je t'y plumerai les pattes;
(Zhe tuh plü-me-ray lay pat;)
Je t'y plumerai les pattes.
Et le dos, et le dos,
Et les ailes, et les ailes,
Et le cou, et le cou,
Et les yeux, et les yeux,
Et le nez, et le nez,
Et le bec, et le bec,
Et la têt', et la têt',
Alouett', Alouett'.
CHORUS

Je t'y plumerai la queue;
(Zhe tuh plü-me-ray la kœ;)
Je t'y plumerai la queue.
Et les pattes, et les pattes,
Et le dos, et le dos,
Et les ailes, et les ailes,
Et le cou, et le cou,
Et les yeux, et les yeux,
Et le nez, et le nez,
Et le bec, et le bec,

Et la têt', et la têt',
Alouett', Alouett'.
CHORUS

COCKLES AND MUSSELS

In Dublin's fair city,
Where girls are so pretty,
'Twas there I first met with sweet Molly Malone.
She drove a wheelbarrow
Through streets broad and narrow,

CHORUS
Crying, "Cockles and mussels, alive, alive-o;
Alive, alive-o,
Alive, alive-o."
Crying, "Cockles and mussels,
Alive, alive-o."

She was a fishmonger,
But sure 'twas no wonder,
For so were her mother and father before.
They drove their wheelbarrows
Through streets broad and narrow,
CHORUS

She died of a fever *(pronounced "fay-ver")*,
And nothing could save her,
And that was the end of poor Molly Malone.
Her ghost wheels a barrow
Through streets broad and narrow,
CHORUS

TZENA, TZENA, TZENA
Words by Mitchell Parish;
Music by Issachar Miron (Michrovsky) and Julius Grossman

Tzena, Tzena, Tzena, Tzena,
How can anything be plainer than
My love for you?
Tzena, Tzena, Tzena, Tzena,
Don't you know your eyes contain a look
That thrills me through?
Tzena, Tzena, ev'ryone is waiting,
For a wedding they're anticipating,
Everyone is happy celebrating,
People dancing in the streets.
Clap your hands and *(clap)*
Raise your voices higher;
Make a circle
While we dance around the fire.
Dance the hora *(clap)*
To your heart's desire;

(continued on next page)

All the world's in
Love with Tzena, Tzena.

WALTZING MATILDA

Words by A. B. Paterson; Music by Marie Cowan

Once a jolly swagman
Camped by a billabong,
Under the shade of a coolibah tree,
And he sang as he watched
And waited till his billy boiled,
"You'll come a-waltzing Matilda with me.
Waltzing Matilda, waltzing Matilda,
You'll come a-waltzing Matilda with me."
And he sang as he watched
And waited till his billy boiled,
"You'll come a-waltzing Matilda with me."

Down came a jumbuck
To drink at that billabong;
Up jumped the swagman and grabbed him with glee.
And he sang as he shoved
That jumbuck in his tucker-bag,
"You'll come a-waltzing Matilda with me.
Waltzing Matilda, waltzing Matilda,
You'll come a-waltzing Matilda with me."
And he sang as he shoved
That jumbuck in his tucker-bag,
"You'll come a-waltzing Matilda with me."

Up rode the squatter
Mounted on his thoroughbred;
Down came the troopers, one, two, three.
"Whose that jolly jumbuck
You've got in your tucker-bag?
You'll come a-waltzing Matilda with me.
Waltzing Matilda, waltzing Matilda,
You'll come a-waltzing Matilda with me."
"Whose that jolly jumbuck
You've got in your tucker-bag?
You'll come a-waltzing Matilda with me."

Up jumped the swagman,
Sprang into the billabong;
"You'll never catch me alive," said he.
And his ghost may be heard
As you pass by that billabong,
"You'll come a-waltzing Matilda with me.
Waltzing Matilda, waltzing Matilda,
You'll come a-waltzing Matilda with me."
And his ghost may be heard

As you pass by that billabong,
"You'll come a-waltzing Matilda with me."

TWINKLE, TWINKLE, LITTLE STAR

Twinkle, twinkle, little star,
How I wonder what you are!
Up above the world so high,
Like a diamond in the sky.
Twinkle, twinkle, little star,
How I wonder what you are!

When the blazing sun is gone,
When he nothing shines upon,
Then you show your little light,
Twinkle, twinkle all the night.
Twinkle, twinkle, little star,
How I wonder what you are!

Parody
Starkle, starkle, little twink,
How I wonder what you think!
Up above the world so high,
Think you own the whole darn sky?
Starkle, starkle, little twink,
You're not so great,
That's what I think!

COMIN' THRU THE RYE

If a body meet a body
Comin' through the rye.
If a body kiss a body;
Need a body cry.
Ev'ry lassie has her laddie,
Nane, they say, ha'e I.
Yet a' the lads they smile on me
When comin' through the rye.

If a body meet a body
Comin' frae the town.
If a body greet a body,
Need a body frown.
Ev'ry lassie has her laddie,
Nane, they say, ha'e I.
Yet a' the lads they smile on me
When comin' through the rye.

THE HOKEY-POKEY

You put your right foot in;
You put your right foot out;
You put your right foot in,
And you shake it all about.
You do the Hokey-Pokey,
And you turn yourself about.
That's what it's all about.

Hey, you put your left foot in;
You put your left foot out;
You put your left foot in,
And you shake it all about.
You do the Hokey-Pokey,
And you turn yourself about.
That's what it's all about.

Hey, you put your right hand in;
You put your right hand out;
You put your right hand in,
And you shake it all about.
You do the Hokey-Pokey,
And you turn yourself about.
That's what it's all about.

Hey, you put your left hand in;
You put your left hand out;
You put your left hand in,
And you shake it all about.
You do the Hokey-Pokey,
And you turn yourself about.
That's what it's all about.

Hey, you put your right shoulder in;
You put your right shoulder out;
You put your right shoulder in,
And you shake it all about.
You do the Hokey-Pokey,
And you turn yourself about.
That's what it's all about.

Hey, you put your left shoulder in;
You put your left shoulder out;
You put your left shoulder in;
And you shake it all about.
You do the Hokey-Pokey,
And you turn yourself about.

That's what it's all about.

Hey, you put your right hip in;
You put your right hip out;
You put your right hip in,
And you shake it all about.
You do the Hokey-Pokey,
And you turn yourself about,
That's what it's all about.

Hey, you put your left hip in;
You put your left hip out;
You put your left hip in,
And you shake it all about.
You do the Hokey-Pokey,
And you turn yourself about.
That's what it's all about.

Hey, you put your whole self in;
You put your whole self out;
You put your whole self in,
And you shake it all about.
You do the Hokey-Pokey,
And you turn yourself about.
That's what it's all about.
Hey!

THE ALLEY CAT SONG
Words by Jack Harlen; Music by Frank Bjorn

He goes on the prowl each night
Like an alley cat,
Lookin' for some new delight
Like an alley cat.
She can't trust him out of sight,
There's no doubt of that.
He just don't know wrong from right,
Like an alley cat.

CHORUS
He meets 'em (meow)
And loves 'em (meow)
And leaves 'em (meow);
That's what Catsanova does.
It's no way to treat a pal;
She should tell him "Scat!"
Aren't you sorry for that gal
With her alley cat?

He goes on the prowl each night
Like an alley cat.
Lookin' for some new delight
Like an alley cat.
He don't know what faithful means,

31

(continued on next page)

There's no doubt of that.
He's too busy makin' scenes
Like an alley cat.
CHORUS

PUT YOUR LITTLE FOOT RIGHT OUT
Words and Music by Larry Spier

Put your little foot,
Put your little foot,
Put your little foot right out.
Put your little foot,
Put your little foot,
Put your little foot right out.
Put your arm around,
Put your arm around,
Put your arm around my waist.
Keep your arm around,
Keep your arm around,
Keep your arm around my waist.
Take a step to the side;
Take a step to the rear;
Take a step to the side,
But forever stay near.
As we dance through the night
And the morning draws near,
By the dawn's early light,
All our cares disappear.
Do a little whirl,
Do a little whirl,
Do a little whirl about.
Do a little twirl,
Do a little twirl,
Do a little twirl about.
Walk a little bit;
Talk a little bit;
Put your little foot right out.
Sing a little bit;
Swing a little bit;
Put your little foot right out.

THE BUNNY HOP
Words and Music by Ray Anthony and Leonard Auletti

Put your right foot forward;
Put your left foot out,
Do the Bunny Hop.
Hop, hop, hop!
Dance this new creation;

It's the new sensation.
Do the Bunny Hop.
Hop, hop, hop!
Let's all join in the fun,
Father, mother, son.
Do the Bunny Hop.
Hop, hop, hop!

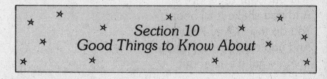

Section 10
Good Things to Know About

THE ALPHABET SONG

A B C D E F G
H I J K L M N O P
Q R S and T U V
W (double-U) and X Y Z.
Now you've heard my A B C;
Tell me what you think of me.

REMEMBER YOUR NAME AND ADDRESS
Words and Music by Irving Caesar

Remember your name and address
And telephone number too.
Then if some day you lose your way,
You'll know just what to do.
Walk up to that kind policeman,
The very first one you meet,
And simply say, "I've lost my way;
I cannot find my street.
But I know my name and address
And telephone number too."
Then he'll be kind
And help you find
The dear ones who wait for you.

THE MULBERRY BUSH

Here we go round the mulberry bush,
The mulberry bush, the mulberry bush.
Here we go round the mulberry bush
So early in the morning.
This is the way we wash our clothes,
We wash our clothes, we wash our clothes.
This is the way we wash our clothes
So early Monday morning.

This is the way we iron our clothes,
We iron our clothes, we iron our clothes.
This is the way we iron our clothes
So early Tuesday morning.
This is the way we scrub the floor,
We scrub the floor, we scrub the floor.
This is the way we scrub the floor
So early Wednesday morning.
This is the way we mend our clothes,
We mend our clothes, we mend our clothes.
This is the way we mend our clothes
So early Thursday morning.
This is the way we sweep the house,
We sweep the house, we sweep the house.
This is the way we sweep the house
So early Friday morning.
This is the way we bake our bread,
We bake our bread, we bake our bread.
This is the way we bake our bread
So early Saturday morning.
This is the way we go to church,
We go to church, we go to church.
This is the way we go to church
So early Sunday morning.

TEN LITTLE INDIANS

One little, two little, three little Indians,
Four little, five little, six little Indians,
Seven little, eight little, nine little Indians,
Ten little Indian boys.

Ten little, nine little, eight little Indians,
Seven little, six little, five little Indians,
Four little, three little, two little Indians,
One little Indian boy.

THIS OLD MAN

This old man, he played one;
He played knick-knack on my thumb.

CHORUS
With a knick-knack, paddy whack,
Give a dog a bone;
This old man came rolling home.

This old man, he played two;
He played knick-knack on my shoe.
CHORUS

This old man, he played three;
He played knick-knack on my knee.
CHORUS

This old man, he played four;
He played knick-knack on my door.
CHORUS

This old man, he played five;
He played knick-knack on my hive.
CHORUS

This old man, he played six;
He played knick-knack on my sticks.
CHORUS

This old man, he played seven;
He played knick-knack up in heaven.
CHORUS

This old man, he played eight;
He played knick-knack on my gate.
CHORUS

This old man, he played nine;
He played knick-knack on my spine.
CHORUS

This old man, he played ten;
He played knick-knack once again.
CHORUS

Section 11
Nursery Rhymes

BILLY BOY

Oh, where have you been, Billy Boy, Billy Boy?
Oh, where have you been, charming Billy?
"I have been to seek a wife;
She's the joy of my life;
She's a young thing and cannot leave her mother."

Did she bid you to come in, Billy Boy, Billy Boy?
Did she bid you to come in, charming Billy?
"Yes, she bade me to come in;
There's a dimple in her chin;
She's a young thing and cannot leave her mother."

Can she make a cherry pie, Billy Boy, Billy Boy?
Can she make a cherry pie, charming Billy?
"She can make a cherry pie,
Quick's a cat can wink her eye;
She's a young thing and cannot leave her mother."

LITTLE BO-PEEP

Little Bo-Peep has lost her sheep
And can't tell where to find them.
Leave them alone and they'll come home,
Wagging their tails behind them.

ROCK-A-BYE, BABY

Rock-a-bye, baby,
On the treetop.
When the wind blows,
The cradle will rock.
When the bough breaks,
The cradle will fall,
And down will come baby,
Cradle and all.

Hush-a-bye, baby,
On the treetop.
When the wind blows,
The cradle will rock.
When the bough breaks,
The cradle will fall,
And down will come baby,
Cradle and all.

SING A SONG OF SIXPENCE

Sing a song of sixpence,
A pocket full of rye;
Four and twenty blackbirds
Baked in a pie.
When the pie was opened,
The birds began to sing.
Wasn't that a dainty dish
To set before the king?
The king was in the countinghouse,
Counting out his money.
The queen was in the parlor,
Eating bread and honey.
The maid was in the garden,
Hanging out the clothes;
Along came a blackbird
And pecked off her nose.

BAA, BAA, BLACK SHEEP

Baa, baa, black sheep,
Have you any wool?
Yes, sir, yes, sir,
Three bags full:
One for my master

And one for my dame,
But none for the little boy
Who lives down the lane.

JACK AND JILL

Jack and Jill went up the hill
To fetch a pail of water.
Jack fell down and broke his crown,
And Jill came tumbling after.

Up Jack got and home he ran
As fast as he could caper;
There his mother bound his head
With vinegar and brown paper.

HOT CROSS BUNS

Hot cross buns!
Hot cross buns!
One a penny, two a penny,
Hot cross buns!
If you have no daughters,
If you have no daughters,
If you have no daughters,
Then give them to your sons.
But if you have none of these little elves,
Then you must eat them all yourselves.

HUMPTY DUMPTY

Humpty Dumpty sat on a wall;
Humpty Dumpty had a great fall.
All the king's horses and all the king's men
Couldn't put Humpty Dumpty together again.

LITTLE JACK HORNER

Little Jack Horner
Sat in a corner,
Eating his Christmas pie.
He stuck in his thumb
And pulled out a plum,
And said "What a good boy am I."

HEY, DIDDLE, DIDDLE

Hey, diddle, diddle,
The cat and the fiddle,
The cow jumped over the moon.
The little dog laughed
To see such sport,
And the dish ran away with the spoon.

LITTLE BOY BLUE

Little Boy Blue, come blow on your horn;
There's sheep in the meadow and cows in the corn.
Where is the boy who looks after the sheep?
He lies in the haystack, fast asleep.

LITTLE MISS MUFFET

Little Miss Muffet
Sat on a tuffet,
Eating some curds and whey.
There came a big spider
And sat down beside her,
And frightened Miss Muffet away.

THERE WAS AN OLD WOMAN WHO LIVED IN A SHOE

There was an old woman who lived in a shoe;
She had so many children, she didn't know what to do.
She gave them some broth without any bread;
She whipped them all soundly and put them to bed.

OATS, PEAS, BEANS AND BARLEY GROW

Oats, peas, beans and barley grow,
Oats, peas, beans and barley grow.
Can you or I or anyone know
How oats, peas, beans and barley grow?

LAZY MARY, WILL YOU GET UP?

Lazy Mary, will you get up,
Will you get up,
Will you get up?
Lazy Mary, will you get up,
Will you get up today?

Oh, no, Mother, I won't get up,
I won't get up,
I won't get up.
Oh, no, Mother, I won't get up,
I won't get up today.

OLD KING COLE

Now, old King Cole was a merry old soul,
And a merry old soul was he.
He called for his pipe,
And he called for his bowl,
And he called for his fiddlers three.
And ev'ry fiddler had a fine fiddle,
And ev'ry fiddler had a fine fiddle,
And a very fine fiddle had he,

And a very fine fiddle had he.
For old King Cole was a merry old soul;
Yes, a merry old soul was he.
He called for his pipe,
And he called for his bowl,
And he called for his fiddlers three.

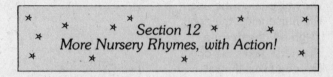

* * Section 12 *
More Nursery Rhymes, with Action!

LONDON BRIDGE

London Bridge is falling down, falling down, falling
   down.
London Bridge is falling down,
My fair lady.
Build it up with iron bars, iron bars, iron bars.
Build it up with iron bars,
My fair lady.
Build it up with gold and silver, gold and silver, gold and
   silver.
Build it up with gold and silver,
My fair lady.
Take the key and lock her up, lock her up, lock her up.
Take the key and lock her up,
My fair lady.

EENSY, WEENSY SPIDER

The eensy, weensy spider
Went up the waterspout.
Down came the rain
And washed the spider out.
Out came the sun
And dried up all the rain.
Now eensy, weensy spider
Went up the spout again.

THE FARMER IN THE DELL

The farmer in the dell,
The farmer in the dell,
Heigh-ho, the derry-o,
The farmer in the dell.
The farmer takes a wife,
The farmer takes a wife,
Heigh-ho, the derry-o,
The farmer takes a wife.
The wife takes the child,

(continued on next page)

The wife takes the child,
Heigh-ho, the derry-o,
The wife takes the child.
The child takes the nurse,
The child takes the nurse,
Heigh-ho, the derry-o,
The child takes the nurse.
The nurse takes the dog,
The nurse takes the dog,
Heigh-ho, the derry-o,
The nurse takes the dog.
The dog takes the cat,
The dog takes the cat,
Heigh-ho, the derry-o,
The dog takes the cat.
The cat takes the rat,
The cat takes the rat,
Heigh-ho, the derry-o,
The cat takes the rat.
The rat takes the cheese,
The rat takes the cheese,
Heigh-ho, the derry-o,
The rat takes the cheese.
The cheese stands alone,
The cheese stands alone,
Heigh-ho, the derry-o,
The cheese stands alone.

HICKORY, DICKORY, DOCK

Hickory, dickory, dock,
The mouse ran up the clock.
The clock struck one;
The mouse ran down,
Hickory, dickory, dock.

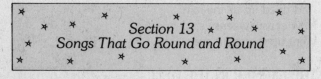

* Section 13 *
Songs That Go Round and Round

THREE BLIND MICE

Three blind mice!
Three blind mice!
See how they run!
See how they run!
They all ran after the farmer's wife,
Who cut off their tails with a carving knife.
Did you ever see such a sight in your life
As three blind mice?

ROW, ROW, ROW YOUR BOAT

Row, row, row your boat
Gently down the stream,
Merrily, merrily, merrily, merrily,
Life is but a dream.

FRÈRE JACQUES

NOTE: First verse in italics gives the pronunciations
of the French words.

Frère Jacques,
Frère Jacques,
Dormez vous,
Dormez vous?
Sonnez les matines,
Sonnez les matines,
Din din don,
Din din don.

Frair-uh Zhah-kuh,
Frair-uh Zhah-kuh,
Dor-may voo,
Dor-may voo?
Sun-nay lay ma-teen-uh,
Sun-nay lay ma-teen-uh,
Dan dan dôn,
Dan dan dôn.

Are you sleeping,
Are you sleeping,
Brother John,
Brother John?
Morning bells are ringing,
Morning bells are ringing,
Ding dong ding,
Ding dong ding.

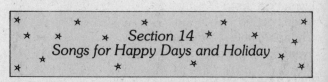

* Section 14 *
Songs for Happy Days and Holiday

RUDOLPH THE RED-NOSED REINDEER
Words and Music by Johnny Marks

You know Dasher and Dancer and Prancer and Vixen,
Comet and Cupid and Donner and Blitzen,
But do you recall
The most famous reindeer of all?
Rudolph the Red-Nosed Reindeer
Had a very shiny nose,

And if you ever saw it,
You would even say it glows.
All of the other reindeer
Used to laugh and call him names;
They never let poor Rudolph
Join in any reindeer games.
Then one foggy Christmas Eve,
Santa came to say:
"Rudolph with your nose so bright,
Won't you guide my sleigh tonight?"
Then how the reindeer loved him
As they shouted out with glee,
"Rudolph the Red-Nosed Reindeer,
You'll go down in history."

SANTA CLAUS IS COMIN' TO TOWN
Words and Music by J. Fred Coots and Haven Gillespie

You better watch out; you better not cry;
Better not pout; I'm telling you why:
Santa Claus is comin' to town.
He's making a list and checking it twice;
Gonna find out who's naughty and nice:
Santa Claus is comin' to town.
He sees when you are sleepin';
He knows when you're awake;
He knows if you've been bad or good;
So be good for goodness sake.
Oh, you better watch out; you better not cry;
Better not pout; I'm telling you why:
Santa Claus is comin' to town.

FROSTY THE SNOW MAN
Words and Music by Steve Nelson and Jack Rollins

Frosty the Snow Man was a jolly, happy soul,
With a corncob pipe and a button nose and two eyes
    made out of coal.
Frosty the Snow Man is a fairy tale, they say;
He was made of snow, but the children know how he
    came to life one day.
There must have been some magic in that old silk hat
    they found,
For when they placed it on his head, he began to dance
    around.
Oh, Frosty the Snow Man was alive as he could be,
And the children say he could laugh and play just the
    same as you and me.

Frosty the Snow Man knew the sun was hot that day,

So he said, "Let's run and we'll have some fun now
    before I melt away."
Down to the village with a broomstick in his hand,
Running here and there all around the square, sayin',
    "Catch me if you can."
He led them down the streets of town right to the
    traffic cop,
And he only paused a moment when he heard
    him holler "Stop!"
For Frosty the Snow Man had to hurry on his way,
But he waved good-bye, sayin', "Don't you cry; I'll be
    back again some day."
Thumpety thump thump,
Thumpety thump thump,
Look at Frosty go;
Thumpety thump thump,
Thumpety thump thump,
Over the hills of snow.

PETER COTTONTAIL
Words and Music by Steve Nelson and Jack Rollins

Here comes Peter Cottontail,
Hoppin' down the bunny trail,
Hippity hoppin', Easter's on its way.
Bringin' ev'ry girl and boy
Baskets full of Easter joy,
Things to make your Easter bright and gay.
He's got jelly beans for Tommy,
Colored eggs for sister Sue.
There's an orchid for your mommy
And an Easter bonnet too.
Oh! here comes Peter Cottontail,
Hoppin' down the bunny trail,
Hippity hoppity, Happy Easter Day.

Here comes Peter Cottontail,
Hoppin' down the bunny trail,
Look at him stop and listen to him say:
"Try to do the things you should."
Maybe if you're extra good,
He'll roll lots of Easter eggs your way.
You'll wake up on Easter morning,
And you'll know that he was there
When you find those choc'late bunnies
That he's hiding ev'rywhere.
Oh! here comes Peter Cottontail,
Hoppin' down the bunny trail,
Hippity hoppity, Happy Easter Day.

(continued on next page)

Year-Round Version

Look at Peter Cottontail,
Hoppin' down the bunny trail,
A rabbit of distinction, so they say.
He's the king of Bunnyland
'Cause his eyes are shiny, and
He can spot the wolf a mile away.
When the others go for clover
And the big bad wolf appears,
He's the one that's watching over,
Givin' signals with his ears.
And that's why folks in Rabbit Town
Feel so free when he's around';
Peter's helpin' someone ev'ry day.

Little Peter Cottontail,
Hoppin' down the bunny trail,
Happened to stop for carrots on the way.
Something told him it was wrong;
Farmer Jones might come along,
And an awful price he'd have to pay.
But he knew his legs were faster,
So he nibbled three or four,
And he almost met disaster
When he heard that shotgun roar.
Oh, that's how Peter Cottontail,
Hoppin' down the bunny trail,
Lost his tail but still he got away.

HONOR YOUR PARENTS
Words and Music by Glenn Wilkinson and Mary Gross

I never have seen me a happier lass
Than one always doin' the things that she's asked.
She joyfully does what her mum and dad say,
And she whistles a tune as she goes on her way.
(whistle)

I never have seen me a happier lad
Than one who's obeying his mother and dad.
He doesn't talk back when he's told what to do,
But he jumps to his work with a click of a shoe.

CHORUS
Honor your parents in ev'ry way
That is pleasin' and true.
You'll have many a happy day,
And that's the promise for you.

So be thankful for all that your mum and dad do,
And do all you can to make them proud of you.
And if you be looking for your pot of gold,
You'll be finding it doing the things you are told.
CHORUS

THE NIÑA, THE PINTA, THE SANTA MARÍA
Words and Music by Ruth Roberts and Bill Katz

There were three little ships in the harbor,
As lonely as they could be,
'Cause nobody wanted to sail them,
Sail them over the sea.
The *Niña (pronounced "Neen-ya"),* the *Pinta,* the *Santa María,*
Sail them over the sea.

Along came a man named Columbus,
Who said that the world was round.
He pleaded with Queen Isabella
To see what ships could be found.
The *Niña,* the *Pinta,* the *Santa María,*
They were the ships that were found.

He filled them with food and with water
And sailors to steer each ship.
The bigger boats laughed in the harbor (ha, ha);
"You'll never finish the trip."
The *Niña,* the *Pinta,* the *Santa María,*
Knew they'd finish the trip.

The ocean was windy and stormy;
The waves were as high as could be.
The load was so heavy to carry,
But on went the brave little three.
The *Niña,* the *Pinta,* the *Santa María,*
On went the brave little three.

At last came the day when Columbus
Sighted America's shore.
Just think he might never have found it
If it hadn't been for
The *Niña,* the *Pinta,* the *Santa María*
Sailed to America's shore.

YANKEE DOODLE

Yankee Doodle went to town a-riding on a pony,
Stuck a feather in his cap and called it macaroni.

CHORUS
Yankee Doodle keep it up,

Yankee Doodle dandy.
Mind the music and the step
And with the girls be handy.

Fath'r and I went down to camp
Along with Captain Goodin.
There we saw the men and boys
As thick as hasty puddin'.
CHORUS

There was Captain Washington
Upon a slapping stallion,
Giving orders to his men;
I guess there were a million.
CHORUS

WE GATHER TOGETHER TO ASK THE LORD'S BLESSING

We gather together to ask the Lord's blessing;
He chastens and hastens His will to make known.

The wicked oppressing now cease from distressing;
Sing praises to His name; He forgets not His own.

Beside us to guide us, our God with us joining,
Ordaining, maintaining His kingdom divine.
So from the beginning the fight we were winning;
Thou, Lord, wast at our side: all glory be Thine!

We all do extol Thee, Thou leader triumphant,
And pray that Thou still our defender wilt be.
Let Thy congregation escape tribulation;
Thy name be ever praised! O Lord, make us free!

HAPPY BIRTHDAY TO YOU
Words and Music by Mildred Hill and Patty Hill

Happy birthday to you,
Happy birthday to you,
Happy birthday, dear *(name)*,
Happy birthday to you.

Reader's Digest has published nine other music books:
Family Songbook, Treasury of Best Loved Songs, Family Songbook of Faith and Joy, Festival of Popular Songs, Great Music's Greatest Hits, The Merry Christmas Songbook, Popular Songs That Will Live Forever, Country and Western Songbook and *Unforgettable Musical Memories.*
You can order them from Reader's Digest, Pleasantville, New York 10570.
(A few songs appear in more than one book,
but the musical arrangements are different.)

Reader's Digest Fund for the Blind is publisher of the Large-Type Edition of *Reader's Digest.* For subscription information about this magazine, please contact Reader's Digest Fund for the Blind, Inc., Dept. 250, Pleasantville, N.Y. 10570.